THE BALLAD OF THE LAZY 'L'

S.R. KRISHNAMMA

The **Ballad**
of the **Lazy 'L'**

*For Bernard & Alice and Sarah
All the best.
Kris.
S.R. Ishram
Goa Dec 2006*

Rani Press
1994

Published by Rani Press
31 South Street
Corsham
Wiltshire
SN13 9HB

© Copyright S.R. Krishnamma 1994

Cover illustration by Naomi Arton
Cover photograph by Kevin Wilkinson

ISBN 0-9523720-0-2

Reprinted June 2000

Typeset in Century 10/12pt by Scriptmate Editions
Manufacture coordinated in UK by Book-in-Hand Ltd
20 Shepherds Hill, London N6 5AH

Preface

This second edition is a dedication to my friend John Wipp who agreed to proof read the manuscript when he was dying from a terminal illness. When he had finished he called me to say, "It's done Kris. Good luck and God bless."

He died the following day.

The manuscript contained some obvious punctuation errors which John had missed. I could have corrected them, but decided not to. It would have been like interfering with the epitaph on a person's grave.

Keep the faith brother. Wherever you may be!

Imagine if you can, a hospital where the sick are taken in and made worse; where legless men are admitted to have their arms amputated; where cases of cholera are infected with small-pox for good measure; and where men who once believed they were Napoleon come out thinking they are Caesar as well. Imagine too, the crazy panel of doctors, consultants, and scientists, who formulate the policies of such a hospital; holding board meetings, attending conferences, issuing directives, pontificating theories; to be passed on to the mindless lower echelons to be implemented.

Could such a gruesome anomaly survive as a credible institution? It does, it thrives, all over the world; and one of the most vigorous and self aggrandizing of its affiliates is called the British penal system. A powerful, politically persuasive unit of society, that encourages the growth of crime while purporting to limit it.

Chapter 1

There was a clear indication in the first words I heard from the escort party of prison officers, that the prison I was being transferred to was different.

As he locked the handcuffs on my wrist the officer had asked, "Not too tight is it, mate?"

I had been held in Winchester first on remand for fourteen months, and then as a convicted prisoner for ten months. During that time I had never heard a prison officer use the word mate, as conversational idiom, to a prisoner. It would have run counter to the policy of a prison whose aim seemed to be to exclude from the vocabulary of those who maintained it any words which hinted at a commonly shared humanity. With one or two exceptions the screws used barks and snarls to make themselves understood. The ambitious ones tried to sneer.

Having never been to prison before, in fact having not been inside a police cell before, I had come to the conclusion that the harsh, repressive, hate-generating attitude of the screws in Winchester Prison was normal for prison officers everywhere.

It therefore took me by surprise to be escorted to my new prison by human beings who had the common social decency to ask if the cuffs on my wrist were too tight.

Even so, I looked at him twice to make sure he was not trying to be sarcastic.

The air of informality continued in the transit van. The officers took off their hats, loosened ties, put their feet up and relaxed. After a while one of them handed me a newspaper he had finished. A small enough gesture, but one which the dogs of Winchester, as the screws there were collectively known to us as, were not programmed to perform.

The relationship between prisoners and those who guard them by any definition is bound to be unequal, but it was the needless provocation and personal malice of the dogs of Winchester that I could not understand. Most of the prison officers at Winchester *enjoyed* being nasty. The policy of the prison suited their temperament exactly. I had given up trying to work out if it was a matter of deliberate policy at Winchester to create animosity. I fantasized that the prison was in the pay of an antagonistic foreign power whose aim was to undermine the community at large by converting men who had committed a criminal act by chance or circumstance, into dedicated units of disruptive social behaviour. Petty offenders left that prison with revolutionary hatred in their eyes.

"Hands out of your fucking pockets! Button your fucking jacket! Get your fucking hair cut: As a convicted prisoner I got used to, and accepted all the invective that came my way. But on remand, dreaming hopefully that I would go free, I clung to that most spurious of English rallying cries that in these islands a man is innocent until proven guilty.

While on remand I daily tried to assert the spirit of that slogan. Daily I was knocked back and ridiculed for believing such fatuous myths.

Why, I asked them, was an innocent man locked up for twenty three hours of the day? Why was his watch taken away from him? Why were his letters censored? And so on. My questions were met with a shrug of the shoulders, cold silences, smirks or jeers. In the end I got tired of asking. Frequently I would point-blank refuse to obey an order and end up in the punishment block. The fairy story that in England a man is innocent until proven guilty died in the dismal, smelly, overcrowded cells of Winchester.[*]

Somewhere I had read or heard the proposition that to really know a country you had to go to its prisons. If Winchester was a mirror of the country, the image was a sorry one that reflected the shapes of swaggering bullies, who only needed the jackboot and whip to be instantly recognised.

Fortunately for me, Britain regularly heads the West European league for putting the most number of its people in prison which meant that there were other prisons besides Winchester. I was being transferred to a dispersal prison in the Midlands. All that I knew about it was that it was a comparatively new, high security, purpose-built prison.

The words 'high security' to describe it made me apprehensive. I did not possess the ability to escape out of a paper bag. The security of Winchester had been more than sufficient to contain me, and that was just a local. High security could mean a harsher, stricter, regime. I just did not know what to expect.

There was one other prisoner going to the same prison; a man

---

[*] The regime in any prison reflects the perspective of The Chief and Governor. The conditions referred to in Winchester prevailed during the years 1973-75.

with a hearing aid who stared out of the window speaking to no one. Being handcuffed to him left me on the inside of the aisle having to twist my head awkwardly to catch a glimpse of the passing countryside.

Shut up in the prison, the perimeter wall had been my only horizon for over a year. I gawped at the fleeting countryside, trees and waving grass, dogs and cows, occasionally a horse or a distant church, as if I had never seen such sights before.

The Senior Officer, white-shirted to denote his rank, was studying our files. Mine had become bulkier since I last saw it. After a while he came over to us. He noticed the way I was straining my head to look out of the window.

"I'm taking the cuffs off you gents," he said, "you can both have a window then. Don't do anything silly and get me into trouble, I'm not supposed to do this."

I guessed he must have learned from our files that we were not escape risks. Even so, it was a gesture to be thankful for; a four hour journey where each time you wanted to pick your nose you had to drag your companion's arm with you becomes tedious.

We passed over a canal bridge and down a country road heavy with summer foliage. Something about the curvature of the road and the way the trees were located on either side sent a painful twinge of recognition through me. It reminded me of the road my home on the Isle of Wight stood on.

A blizzard of thoughts and the nostalgic images they provoked raged through me as it had on other occasions since this prison nightmare had started.

My wife Daisy, my family, two boys, two girls; I savoured their names on my mind's tongue briefly. Jesus what have I done? All gone. Where is this going to end? How will Daisy manage? What's to become of Newclose? Will she have to sell it? How are my kids really taking it? I see the smiling faces they show me on visits, but I can also sense that Daisy has rehearsed them in the waiting room before they came in. Her skills as a school teacher would have helped her to impress upon them the need to keep my morale high. I thought of my dog Poppy, so soft and friendly, it could play with ducklings and kittens without hurting them. She would be dead by the time I got out.

If by some miracle I had been granted my freedom on that strange country road I knew I would never break the law again. I would have learned my lesson. There is an optimum sentence for every violation of the law; a punishment that is variable in time. It may be a month for one man, a year for another, or several years for a third—all for the same crime. At the end of this optimum period there is no purpose in terms of reformation or punishment in keeping the prisoner in captivity any longer. He is now ready to change. He has been brought right up to the exact point where he may be turned around: reclaimed for society.

All the professions most concerned with the prisoner, the ones who pass the laws and uphold them, policemen, judges, and prison officials, haven't the faintest idea when the prisoner is in this mutable condition. Only the prisoner knows when this crucial time has arrived.

After two years of confinement in various moods of Her Majesty's displeasure, I knew I had reached that watershed.

Sitting in that van I daydreamed of a more poetically just society where judges and those they had sentenced were brought together annually for an informal exchange of views. Naturally some sort of moat filled with razor wire, or live crocodiles, might have to be placed between them to prevent the judge from perpetrating any more of his perverted fantasies on the prisoner. But at least some earthy, honest, dialogue could be conducted between men of flesh and blood away from the hideous pretensions of the court room, in which human beings are cloaked and bewigged according to rank, disguised and costumed and speaking in a ritual abracadabra, acting out a dramatic charade which they fondly call equity. Some of them attack while others defend. The next day when they have another prisoner to play with, they change cloaks and attitudes, and perform the opposite function.

I felt confident that if I could have talked to the judge right then about my theory of optimum sentences I would convince him that my time was up and I could go free and live harmlessly ever after. Two years was the optimum sentence, not ten. That was an overkill five times over. The extra eight years would be counter-productive; either I would become institutionalised into a vegetable, no good to myself, my family or the state, or I would harden into a professional criminal, no good to myself, my family, or the state.

It was a painful line in fantasies, we were already in sight of the prison. The officers were putting on their hats and adjusting jackets giving all the indications that the journey was over.

One of them pointed.

"There she be," he said. A low-lying building of three storeys which looked like a modern factory was in fact the prison; later when I knew it better I got used to calling it the Lazy L. Knowing what it was helped me to follow the outline of the high curving wall that surrounded it. The perimeter of a factory would not have been quite so high nor would it have been built in quite such an unbroken way.

We turned into a gravel road and up to the prison gates. An officer on duty in a glass fronted cubicle nodded in recognition to the van driver and spoke into an intercom.

A few seconds later an electronically operated outer entrance edged slowly open like a garage door and the van entered a holding area. As the outer door slowly shut behind us, and I watched the last chink of light disappear behind me, I knew it would be a long time before it was opened for me again.

At least in that, I was right.

Chapter 2

Being transferred from Winchester to the Lazy L was a culture shock in reverse. The pleasant surprises began from the time I was kitted out for my life as a high-security prisoner.

In exchange for our civilian clothes, we got jeans, flannel trousers, striped shirts, tee shirts, and black slip-on shoes. The most satisfying innovation was that I was allowed to keep my own socks, towel, and underwear. Strangely, the most identity-destroying element of wearing prison clothes is not what you see, but that which is most intimate and hidden. Communal underwear was especially degrading.

The Senior Officer going through my carrier bag of personal belongings also allowed me to keep my sun glasses, world atlas, and training shoes. The reason given to me at Winchester for withholding the atlas was that maps appertaining to say Bangladesh, or South Korea, could be useful in an escape attempt. The reason for not letting prisoners keep their training shoes was that they would be able to run faster in them while escaping, and of course sun glasses could be used to disguise one's appearance. It was the result of that sort of serpentine reasoning, incorporated into the rules of the prison, and thereby immune to discussion or reason, that had finally driven me into a stoical silence, and the conclusion that prisons in Britain were run by cretins, albeit powerful ones. I was having to revise that opinion at the Lazy L.

Coming from Winchester to the Lazy L was like crossing the border from a poverty stricken police state into a land of abundance and permissiveness. Yet it was only a move from one prison to another. Before my prison days were over, that theme of relative servitude, or freedom, would be impressed upon me many times, and in many different ways.

On the way over to C wing to which I had been allocated, I noticed the close-circuit cameras situated at strategic points. They were so unobtrusive, that even on that first day I forgot their existence. Apart from the cameras the other sign of custom-built modernity were the electronic locks on the gates. The escorting officer spoke into an intercom and a muffled voice swore at him in jocular style, and the gate was unlocked with an audible click.

We were met at the entrance to C wing by a very tall officer with a drooping Zapata moustache.

"Krishnamma," he said. "Good guess wasn't it? He had an obvious Welsh accent, and an agreeable manner. "Did I pronounce your name right?" he asked.

"Perfect," I replied.

"Right, now then, since there seems to be no one else about I suppose I'll have to be the reception committee, and give you a run down on the place. It's all very simple really. In a nutshell, you can do as you bloody well please here, as long as you don't try to escape, or assault prison officers, especially me. Got that?"

"Got it," I said.

"Follow me," he said, and went into a small office. He selected a key from a row.

"No objection to the ground floor I hope," he asked. "Sounds like a hotel don't it?"

After Winchester I had to agree that it did.

"It'll take you a while but you'll get used to it. Most inmates do. The only ones who don't are the ones who want things to stay as they were."

He led me a few yards down a short spur on the same landing and stopped in front of number 5.

A thickset prisoner wearing overalls covering a ponderous belly came out of one of the other cells. He gave me a studied but friendly look.

"Orright mate?" he asked.

"Fine," I replied.

"Have nothing to do with him," the screw said, "he's what we call a subversive. Thinks England are going to beat Wales on Saturday, in Cardiff Arms Park of all places. Nutty as a fruit cake."

"Never mind about nutty," big belly laughed loudly. "Just you stock up on the Mars bars, me old son, I'll have 'em off you on Saturday."

Just as the screw was about to put the key into the lock he stopped. He handed me the key with a flourish as though he was presenting a bouquet. "Like buying a new house isn't it?" he said, taking my pillow case of kit, and radio.

I inserted the key and opened the door. The significance of that moment was not lost on me; it caused a quiver in my equilibrium. Apart from not having to perform that everyday, very forgettable function for over a year, the key as an object had taken on a symbolism it had never possessed before. What had once been an instrument to open and shut lock mechanisms, had become invested with sinister powers, to spiritually devastate, and debilitate the strongest spirit. There is something so daunting, so inexpressibly final, about being locked up in a box of steel and stone, where there is no keyhole or handle on the inside.

Impressed on my memory of sounds is the unique one of a prison door being beaten from the inside with a chair. The resonance of that appeal, crashing and echoing down platforms and stair wells of iron and steel, is not one that is easily forgotten. Once at Winchester when every other avenue of expression seemed closed, I had picked up a chair and hammered the steel door. When I was done, emotionally drained, physically exhausted, with tears dried on my face, I returned to my bed feeling strangely purified and clean.

Now, here at the Lazy L a prison officer, that species of the human kind that I had thought were the sole guardians of that implement of captivity, was giving it to me.

"Don't lose it," the screw said, "50p fine if you do. By the way what do you want to be called on the wing? Christian name or surname?"

"Call me Kris," I said. "And you?"

"The lads call me Taff. After you've unpacked your gear, come by the office and I'll take details of your diet and religion. OK?"

I went in to my new home. It was small but compact, and had all the necessities; bed, table, chair, hanging space for clothes, built-in unit with cupboards and drawers, notice board for photographs, and even a book shelf. It had recently been cleaned and there was a smell of polish in the air. On the table there was a plastic plate, mug, and bowl in matching blue, and a plastic knife, fork and spoon, in white. They gave an expectant, welcoming aspect to the room. I had been in boarding houses on the outside that had been much worse.

"I checked this one over yesterday." It was the prisoner with the out size belly, holding an outsize jug of tea in his hand.

He introduced himself as George, and poured me a cup. We chatted for a while, the small talk of prisoners anywhere. He asked me how long I was doing and where I came from.

In telling people the length of my sentence, and what I had done to deserve it, I had become used to exclamations of incredulity. Occasionally, behind the air of commiseration, I scented a whiff of scepticism, as though I was holding something back.

Quite naturally, there were some prisoners who claimed to have committed crimes with a higher status value in prison than they actually had.

A man at Winchester had been scalded with boiling water when it was realised that he was not the car thief he purported to be; but had been convicted for sexual offences against children. Before that he had played for the prison volley ball team, and was thought of as one of the lads.

I was not disconcerted when George looked surprised.

"What, ten years for bringing in cannabis! How many people did you kill doing it?"

"There were no bodies, no one got hurt," I said.

"Bit of smack or coke?"

As a means of not having to answer the same old questions on a subject that had become tiresome, I had kept a small file of newspaper clippings about the trial and subsequent sentence.

"There was nothing like that," I said, "it was just cannabis, nothing else. It's all in there." I indicated the file which had spilled out on to the bed from the pillow case of belongings I had brought in with me.

Despite his questions George had a cheerful expressive sense of humour, and I found it relaxing and easy to talk to him. He lived two doors away on the other side of the spur and said he was a sort of unofficial, part-time cleaner on the landing. I asked him about the prison. His answer was unequivocal. He said it was the best prison in Britain.

"Just keep your head down, and do your bird, and the years will just fly by," he said.

After he had left, I sat for a while on the unmade bed, and rolled myself a cigarette. My recently awarded towel was on my lap. The door was open. In a short while I would be able to go through that door and lock it behind me. I could have a shower, then return to open it again. Even in those first few minutes of acquaintanceship with my allocated cell, I felt a sense of dominion, a restoration of the territorial instinct. This was going to be MY home. This room was going to be MINE. I had a key to the front door to prove my proprietorship. It was a feeling I had never experienced in prison before.

I began to visualise the sort of curtains and bedspread that would suit the room. I had also been told that prisoners were allowed to cook on the wing, and replace the plastic substitutes with real crockery. I started to compose some sentences of a letter I intended to write to Daisy later on that day, asking her to send me in a few pots and pans.

I started to feel fine. The life force of optimism began to flow in me again. Irrepressibly, it suggested that I should squeeze the penal system to get as much out of it as I could.

First, an A level in English Literature, maybe even a degree; get fit, learn to cook, and play the guitar, and start some sort of systematic reading of books on parapsychology.

By being transferred to the Lazy L I felt I had a chance of attempting some of these ventures. At least it was good to have cleared the hateful shadow of Winchester prison.

The first week had been allocated as an induction and orientation period, and during that time I learned more about my surroundings.

Taff had taken me round the prison on the second day, and pointed out the main features of interest: gymnasium, playing fields, hospital, shop units, canteen, kitchen, library, stores and so on.

At the end of our tour we stopped at an office and I was given one pound fifty pence in silver; a week's wages in advance. To have real money—even though it was only coins jingling in my pocket, was another humanising touch. These privileges, denied at Winchester; would take a while to lose their glamour. "All that's missing here is the swimming pool, sauna and disco," I said.

"Don't say I said so," he said, "but the name of the game here is 'containment'. No more no less. As long as we keep the inmates behind these walls, without riots or escapes, for whatever sentence they're doing, they can have what they like, within reason of course. If it was up to me I'd have you blokes digging the swimming pool tomorrow. Only the experts would have to come from outside, the rest of the manpower is right here."

That evening when the doors were electronically opened after the hour-long bang-up for tea, I went to see what the entertainment section of the wing had to offer.

There were three leisure rooms. One was reserved for the showing of videos of such sickening nastiness that it was always full. The next was a television room with three or four men watching a nature programme. In the third room I made a stunning discovery. At the end of a day of surprises it clinched my opinion that if I had to be in prison this was the one to be in.

A crudely printed sign on the flap end of a cardboard box was stuck on the outside of the door. It said, CASINO. Inside, a group of men were hunched over a table playing cards. There were small piles of coins in front of them. The dealer was a diminutive, grubby looking fellow with long greasy hair that hung like muddy rivulets on his back. He had a spatulate nose, under which an explosion of blackened and broken teeth were exhibited in a grimace of what seemed to be welcome. He spoke in a low, croaky voice.

"Come in,' come in," he said, shuffling the cards. "New man on the wing. Play poker do you?"

As questions go it was like asking a priest if he knew how to pray, or a donkey if it could bray. I had been playing poker since I was seven years old; had in fact learned the game literally at my father's knee. Since that time, I had played it in several countries, and for a time in England when I had worked in a casino, I had played poker semi-professionally, and made a living at it.

I sidled up to the table, resisting an impulse to acclaim it like a long lost lover and shower it with kisses.

"Is that the game where you have pairs, and threes, and things like that?" I asked.

"You got it," the dealer smirked around the table. His tone had the inviting quality of the wolf asking Red Riding Hood to come in for supper.

"Tell me," I asked, as I pulled up a chair to join the game, "does two pairs beat a full house?"

By the end of that evening the one pound fifty in my pocket had increased to four pounds.

If I could have seen into the future, I would have known that in a few years the scruffy little ragamuffin who was dealing and I would become good friends. His name was Joe Palazzi, known throughout the Lazy L as Joe Fellatio. In the years to come when we reminisced about events in our mutual past, about the men who had come and gone on the wing, he would invariably say, "I'll never forget the day you come through the door of the card room, and asked if two pairs beat a full house, you bastard."

From that first occasion I earned and maintained a reputation for winning consistently at poker on C wing. Whatever the game, draw or stud, Maltese Cross or One-eyed Jacks, as long as it was some form of poker, I knew the percentages by heart. It was simply a question of adhering to them—the rest was just mathematics.

I could never have imagined that a skill such as that, cosmetic by nature, honed and polished in innumerable venues of gambling, over countless hours of tedious watching and waiting; that such a pastime, applicable to the non-essential part of a person's life, and one which I had dismissed as being useless to me during my prison term, would amazingly be catapulted into my life again. Throughout my time at the Lazy L as long as poker was played on the wing, the wages I was paid by the prison were an insignificant part of my total earnings.

By the end of the first week I had bought myself a guitar from poker winnings. Also by the end of the first week I had enrolled in the A level English Literature, and Spanish classes. I had even visited the gymnasium and struggled through half a set of badminton, at the end of which I was weakened to the point of nausea. But it was an exercise which served to strengthen my resolve to get fit. With these initial plans suggesting a positive use of my time in prison I should have been able to view the future with tranquillity. But the future was not as clear as that. It was overshadowed by a threat.

The threat was a simple one. At the end of my week of acclimatisation, the prison authorities had the notion that in payment for all the fine facilities, I would work in one of their shops for eight hours a day. I had seen the shops, and had decided that under no circumstances would I oblige them.

Chapter 3

Taff escorted me to work on the first day. It was mid-September, a day between summer and autumn. A patina of dew covered the grass.

My brain was working at a tremendous rate of ergs trying to figure out a way of avoiding work in the shops. So far it had not produced anything that suggested a workable plan.

The Lazy L was classed as a semi-industrial prison. It produced denim, and finished articles of light engineering. These two shops, the weavers and the light engineers employed about two-thirds of the labour force. Most of the remaining third worked towards the maintenance of the prison: kitchens, laundry, hospital, library and education. There was another very small group of prisoners who were classed under the generic heading of cleaners. They emptied the rubbish, and kept the corridors and grounds of the prison clean.

This last group had much more leisure time than the others. As a consequence they were paid less. Even so, they managed to look better dressed and more affluent than the others. They wore specially tailored jeans, and well laundered T shirts and pullovers.

It was obvious that these people did not wholly rely on their prison wages.

A high proportion of them were Londoners, and within that proportion, they were mostly a group vaguely described as London gangsters.

I had decided that a job like that would suit me; minimum work, maximum leisure, with a little gymnasium and academic study thrown in. Poker, or some other devious enterprise would have to subsidise my wages.

It was not going to be easy getting that kind of a job. Not only was there a waiting list of about a year, but the afore-mentioned London gangsters seemed to think their territory was being poached if someone who came from outside their little patch got a job on the cleaners.

Having no plan, I offered no resistance to the allocation board when they told me I was to start work in the weavers' shop.

The workshops lay about a hundred metres away from the living quarters. They formed an L shape, and as we approached the base we could hear a muffled, clattering noise, like a thousand mad

19

Spaniards clicking their castanets at once, without harmony or pattern.

I had the spark of an idea when I heard that noise. I stopped abruptly and put on what I hoped was an alarmed and anxious look.

"What's the matter?"' Taff asked.

"What is that noise?" I asked fearfully.

"That's where I'm taking you," he replied. That's the weavers.

"Does that noise go on all the time," I enquired.

"'Fraid so. Seven hours a day non-stop. What's more it gets worse when we go inside. It's the one duty shift I do my best to get out of if I can. After about an hour I get a shocking headache," he said.

I grabbed at that information gratefully. "I'm exactly the same," I said. "Right across my eyes. I don't think I could work in a place like that."

"Can't help you there," Taff said. "My job is just to get you to work on the first day. After that it's up to you what you do. Tell you what I can do though—when you get back on the wing for lunch come and see me and I'll give you a labour change form. Fill that in, and you may get a change of labour next week."

In Taff I felt I had found an ally, especially since we were both noise-sensitive people. I hoped he would put in a good word for me with whoever decided changes of labour.

As he had predicted, once inside the weavers shop the noise level changed dramatically. The sound of castanets being played by demented Spaniards gave way to an approximation of the noise caused by an army of men fighting each other with cricket bats. I did not have to feign any discomfort; it came naturally. I did not know what it was in decibels, but I did not like it at all.

Rows of machines, in what looked like a long hangar, banged away incessantly. The pyramid of light above them that apexed at the source was fogged by a grey mist.

"What's that?" I shouted at Taff.

"What's what?" he shouted back.

"That over there," I shouted.

"What over where," he shouted back.

We continued this nonsense conversation for a few minutes before he was able to explain. The grey smog over the machines was a mixture of fluff, nap, and particles of dust, that were being beaten out of the denim being spun on the flat bed of the machines. Over some machines which seemed to be clapping and hammering harder and faster than the others, the haze was so thick one could hardly see through it.

I made a promise to myself. I would have to be physically chained down to one of those machines before I would breathe that air for seven hours a day.

It may be that Taff read some of that intention on my face. He put his hand on my shoulder and shouted in my ear.

"Don't do anything silly. You seem a reasonable bloke. Come and see me in the lunch break and I'll try and sort something out."

He left me in an office where three men were sitting drinking tea. A pasty faced man wearing glasses, and a prominent wart on his left cheek, got up and came towards me.

Inside the office the machine noise was only slightly diminished; the army of men wielding cricket bats had got down to hand-to-hand combat with smaller sporting equipment, like ping-pong bats.

The pasty-faced man introduced himself as the civilian foreman of the shop. He pointed to a bench outside.

"Sit over there. I'll come and see you in a minute," he said. He had an important, 'I am very busy, and don't want to be bothered with you,' air about him.

I sat at the long wooden bench and studied the graffiti that had been carved into the wood. It was predominantly the work of a single dissident. His main observation was that prison-officers were a sub-porcine grouping whose staple diet was excrement. He further alleged that you could always recognise a prison officer by his brown lips; a result of his eating habits.

After about twenty minutes I noticed that the pasty-faced man was still chatting away pleasantly to his friends, so I decided to look around the shop.

At the other end of the shop a very muscular Rastafarian was having a hectic time keeping several machines on the go at the same time. I could tell right away that he was an important man in the shop, a star worker. He had more grey fluff in his hair than anybody else. His hairstyle was ideally suited as a fluff-catcher. One got the impression that he had recently fallen into an open bag of eiderdown. He had been pointed out to me on C wing as an unofficial spokesman for the blacks.

We bellowed a few pleasantries at each other. While we were doing this the pasty-faced foreman came by tapping a pencil on a clipboard.

He nodded at the Rastaman, then gave me a look which suggested he had met me somewhere before, but did not know where, and the circumstances had not been favourable. It was a look that was hesitantly poised between recognition and suspicion. I did not enlighten him, just pointed at the machine, with a suitable mime, as though I was discussing an engineering point, and shouted some gibberish into his ear.

During the five days I was in that shop I saw the foreman twice a day. Each time he had that same perplexed look, trying to remember where he knew me from. Each time I expected him to recognise me, but he never made the connection.

In the tea break the Rastaman whose name was Luke gave me an informative lecture on the politics and infrastructure of the weavers shop. For a start, he said the pasty-faced foreman was of no account; he did not have a clue about what was happening in the shop.

That much I had gathered for myself.

He said it was the blacks in general, and he Luke in particular, who ran the shop. He looked around the tea drinkers. The predominantly black bench we were sitting at, nodded in agreement.

He went on to outline how he could better my life. For the first six months I could be a trainee under him. All I had to do was squirt oil on to the private parts of a machine he would introduce me to when it appeared to be on heat. After six months of such foreplay, I would be permitted to touch it in a more intimate way. Then, although he didn't come right out and say so, just made a vague rolling gesture with his hands and eyes, to indicate the passing years, I too might one day have as much grey fluff in my hair and lungs as he had.

I did not accept his offer, nor did I reject it. As best I could I expressed diffidence at the prospect of holding such high office. More than ever I was determined to get out of that shop.

I had received some unfortunate news from the teacher of the A level English Literature class. Apparently the examining board for the Birmingham area was different to the one at Winchester.

That meant that the years study I had put in at Winchester was wasted. I now had a new set of six books to study, and the exam was only a few weeks away.

At first the teacher had said I would have to wait until the next year, but I groused and grumbled so effectively, that he finally agreed to give me a couple of test questions on one of the books. I had a week in which to prepare the essays. The book was *Two Cheers for Democracy* by EM Forster, and I was aware of it lapping against my thigh in the pocket of my overalls. Since the foreman had forgotten who I was, I decided to keep out of his way in case he suddenly remembered and gave me a job. For the week I was there I took up residence in the five toilets of the shop; flitting from one to the other like a grey butterfly of the bogs, clutching a paperback in one hand,

and my nose with the other. I managed to read the book and compose the essays in among the worst smells of the weavers shop. As a conditioned-reflex, in memory of that time, it is a wonder that I do not urinate instantly on the floor whenever the name of E.M. Forster enters the conversation. It was as well I got a move out of the weavers when I did; already there were whispered suggestions about the new Paki who favoured the ambience of latrines. One or two habitues of the toilets had started to give me secretive smiles of welcome, as though they recognized a fellow traveller on the forbidden olfactory trail.

During the lunch break on the first day I had filled in the labour change forms under Taff's guidance. On Friday, he waved a piece of paper at me. A change of labour had been granted; I was to report to the Light Engineers on the following Monday. Taff looked so pleased about having helped me that I did not have the heart to tell him that a move to the Light Engineers was merely changing from one frying pan to another.

And so it proved—a worse frying pan. The noise in decibels may not have been higher, but it was qualitatively different, and to my ears more painful. The prevailing sound of wooden slats being banged together gave way to the sound of metal being tortured in various ways. There was a machine that made the sound of stones being thrown into a fan with metal blades. Another machine cut sheets of metal into long strips. This treatment made the metal scream all day long. I began to think almost nostalgically about the sound of cricket bats in collision.

As was the custom, I was escorted to work on the first day. A pasty faced man wearing glasses, and a prominent wart on his left cheek, introduced himself as the foreman. At this point I thought had begun one of those pointless dreams that recur and go on all night without chronology or consequence. I fully expected him to point to a bench, and tell me to sit there until he could see me.

In fact he pointed to a bench outside the office.

"Sit over there, I'll see you in a minute," he said. I went outside to the bench, checking the workshop over to see where the toilets were situated. I felt I knew how to play this game. This time I had Messrs Chaucer and Shakespeare, waiting to jump out of my overall pockets.

This was not to be. He came over as promised. His manner was energetic, and bustling, in contrast to his clone at the weavers shop. He asked me a few tricky questions, designed as he claimed, to test my intelligence, such as my name and what I had eaten for breakfast.

"Good, good," he beamed. "We need someone with a bit of intelligence for this one. I've got just the job for you."

He took me along to the part of the shop where the machine was tearing up the sheet-metal. We entered an area that had been caged off as though dangerous animals were housed there. It was tea break time, and the sheet metal had stopped screaming.

"This is it," he said, patting a dormant lump of metal about the size of a small car, that vaguely resembled a giant-sized sewing machine. The visible moving parts were situated where the needle would have been.

"Good, good, you're just the man for this job. No problem counting?" he asked.

"Counting?" I echoed.

"Yes, y'know, one, two, three, four."

"One, two, three, four," I repeated.

It flashed across my mind that if this job demanded any arithmetical calculations, I could pretend to be innumerate, and get out of it that way.

"Yes, nice easy job. As long as you fill your quota." He called to another man in a white coat who was passing by. "You can take that vacancy off the board," he said. "I've got a right, I mean I've got the right man on it now."

He rubbed his hands briskly and sat down in front of the machine. He addressed it as though it was a grand piano, and he was about to play a grand concerto on it. He also massaged his fingers and cracked his knuckles'.

"Good, good," he began, "now before I explain how this machine works," he paused to stroke it affectionately, "it has always been my policy to put my blokes in the full picture. I want them to know why they are doing what they are doing. It's no good asking a bloke to churn out thousands of bits without giving him some sort of "...he paused as though he expected me to finish the sentence.

"Job incentive," I suggested, and immediately wished I hadn't. He favoured me with a smile of dazzling insincerity. For a moment I feared he was going to embrace me.

"Marvellous, brilliant, wah!" he exclaimed. "You've got the hang of it right away. Good, good. Now, most of this shop is geared to making beds for the Saudi Arabian army. You know where that is?"

"No. I don't know where the Saudi Arabian army is," I replied.

"Good, good. Now this machine turns this," (he held up a thin metal rod about 5 cm long) into this," (he held up another rod shaped like an S.)

"Now you may well ask, so what?"

"So what," I asked.

"Good question," he said. "Now let me tell you that this," he held up the S shaped rod aloft as though it was a trophy, "is what holds the whole contraption together. Without this the Saudis wouldn't have a bed to sleep in."

He laughed confidently.

"Good, good. Now if you come and stand behind my shoulder, I'll show you how it works."

He picked up a straight bit, inserted it into a groove, and guided the sewing machine needle end into place. He then stamped vigorously on what looked like the brake pedal of a car and absolutely nothing happened. He stamped on it again.

"Helps if you switch the bloody thing on," he reminded himself, as he depressed a red button on its side. The machine started to vibrate purposefully. This time when he stamped the pedal it gave a hiss, then a cough, and an S bit was born in front of our eyes.

"See what I mean," he said, doing it a few times at high speed to impress me.

"Incredible!" I breathed.

I sat down and had a go. It worked, even for me. Normally machines cease to work as soon as I take over the controls. This was terrible. I looked around in alarm like an animal who sees its avenue of escape being closed.

"I know exactly what you're thinking," he said. "You're wondering about the quota, and how much you can earn. Good, good. Now then this is how it works. The basic wage is one pound fifty pence. To earn that you have to process several zillion, many million, and forty eight bits a week." This figure he uttered so quickly that it blurred before it reached my brain. "After that it's bonus time," he exclaimed joyously. "For every extra .8 of a zillion you process, you get an extra 10 pence. The last bloke who worked here got so rich he retired and bought himself a bungalow in Bognor Regis."

He laughed confidently.

After the foreman had left I sat for a while looking at the machine which I had already nicknamed the beast. It was hate at first sight. When I finally addressed it, I did so not with the sympathies of a piano player, but with the calculating eyes of a professional saboteur. My intention was to wreck it at the earliest opportunity so that it would never again give birth to another S bit.

Chapter 4

Wrecking the beast was easier thought than done. Instinctively, I wanted to do something spontaneous and playful, like smashing its insides with a hammer. Apart from the security arrangements which encased all fragile parts in corsets of steel, I was also assailed by a bout of good sense, a faculty that is not abundant in me. I had already lost nearly three months remission for not being a model prisoner at Winchester. When I got caught for vandalising the beast, as was inevitable, since going berserk with a hammer in a busy workshop cannot be performed furtively, I would certainly lose more remission, and worse, I could be shanghaid* out of a prison which had so many agreeable privileges and facilities.

The first day of my partnership with the beast, I took seriously. I wanted to find out, as a matter of academic interest, if, with the best will in the world, I could produce several zillion, many million, and forty-eight S bits a week, as the foreman had suggested could be accomplished by a man working at average speed.

So the beast and I began a modest duet. I said stamp, and the beast said hiss, cough. Each completed refrain produced an S bit, still warm from its birth, which I placed in a cardboard box.

By lunch time I had established some sort of rhythmic pattern to my task. An impromptu melody was added: stamphiss cough pause, stamphisscough pause, stamphisscough pause, and so on endlessly every five seconds, or seventy two times an hour, which eventually produced a sort of machine stupor.

Hours after the days work had ended, my right leg would involuntarily go into a kind of high-stepping Zulu dance routine, especially, because of some similarity in physical co-ordination, when I was climbing stairs. People using the stairs at the same time would invariably look on the step to see the mashed insect I had so viciously stamped on. "Missed it", I would mutter to myself, as I struggled to keep my leg in order.

There were other side effects. Feigning headaches due to the noise had been my way of getting out of the weavers shop. I had put that in writing on the labour change form. To support that claim I had visited the hospital once or twice a day for a tot of Paracetamol. At

* Shanghaid—transferred suddenly without warning.

the Light Engineers I continued my visits to the hospital. As though I had offended the gods of industry by my earlier deceit, these headaches were now real. The cause was situated right next to my place of work: the machine that sawed up metal sheets into strips. The screeching of that metal had exactly the right amount of anguish to induce a headache in minutes.

I mentioned this to the foreman, doing a mime to portray an expanding and contracting head.

"Good, good," he said, "soon get used to a bit of noise." After three days I had reached the end of the line with the beast. I had not been able to get Messrs Chaucer and Shakespeare out once during that time. The exam was due in just over two weeks, and I was getting panicky. By the end of the third day I had ascertained that if I worked flat out all day, every day, I would just about manage to fill the quota.

I had set my mind on getting an A level in English Literature. It was more than just an academic qualification for me; it would signify to me, and especially to my wife, that this prison sentence was not going to break me; that I could pursue a course of study with discipline, and finish it, as I'd never finished anything in the outside world. I needed a few hours during the day to read the books analytically, if I was going to pass.

I decided to see the first week out. Then on the following Monday I intended to refuse to go to work. That would mean the punishment block for a few days. There, hopefully, I would have the days of silence to understand the language of Chaucer and Shakespeare. Not having a tutor to help me, I had only footnotes and disembodied expositors to rely on. Frequently I found an original passage easier to understand than the pages purporting to explain it.

The crux of the problem was the fact that I had to sit in front of the beast all day long stamping a pedal. If I had been left to my own devices as at the Weavers I could have carried on with my reading, and somehow bodged through the exam. Although the punishment block held no terrors for me, the prospect of going down there was still not a pleasant one.

With that thought predominant, I was kicking the pedal in a desultory fashion one day, when help came to me through two strange forms.

"Boring 'ennit?" The speaker was a powerfully built, wild, piratical, and hairy guy. He had no front teeth, and his eyes were crossed.

The singlet he wore showed his body to be covered in a mixture of coarse black hair and tattoos. The tattoos seemed to have been self-inflicted jobs, except the one on his left forearm which said, 'Ride to live, live to ride'. With a Scandinavian double-horned helmet on his head he would have looked ready for a bit of pillage and rape. His companion was a skeleton in clothes. He had long wispy hair held together with an elastic band, and dreamy eyes which he kept closed most of the time, opening them only when it was absolutely necessary. I had already met them on C wing and knew them as Dirty Harry the Hells Angel, and Slippery.

"It's worse than boring, it's sending me round the bend," I said. Slippery opened his eyes.

"Got any drugs?" he asked. "Got ready cash," he added.

I shook my head. Slippery lost interest, closed his eyes, and seemed to fall asleep standing up.

"We done this job for six months," Dirty Harry said.

"We?" I asked.

"Yeah. I done the stamping, and he done the counting," he said. Slippery opened his eyes.

"Got any drugs for sale?" he asked.

"Don't mind him," Dirty Harry said. "He ain't well." He tapped his head.

"Astral," Slippery explained. "Right on," I said. Slippery fell asleep again.

"What beats me," Dirty Harry continued, "is why they keep on making these bits."

He picked up a handful, the produce of several minutes of passionate stamping, and tossed them over his shoulder like salt. I was about to remonstrate when he added, "There's millions of them over there in tea chests."

He went on to explain. The final assembly section that put together all the bits and pieces to make a completed bed had filled its order two months previously. They were now doing something else. In a nutshell, the Saudi Arabian army had been comfortably bedded down a while ago. I had been creating thousands of S bits which would never be consummated in any act of bed making.

"So where are these tea chests?" I asked. Dirty Harry took me along to show me. It was as he had said. At the end of the shop where the cobwebs hung out, there were dozens of tea chests lying about in no particular order. Eight of them were overflowing with S bits. A ninth one was half full; it was presumably the one into which the foreman was flinging my days produce.

"See what I mean?" Dirty Harry said, picking up a handful and tossing them over his shoulder like salt.

"I'm beginning to get the whole picture," I said, picking up a handful and tossing them over my shoulder like salt. It gave me a grand profligate feeling. I filled the pockets of my overall with S bits and made my way back to the beast. I emptied them into my out-tray cardboard box and went to the toilet to read my books.

The following day I became more systematic. The foreman had established a pattern of visiting me twice a day: once before the lunch break, and once before the final bell. At these times he would pick the box of S bits and disappear towards the far end of the shop. I kept track of his movements from a discreet distance. When he flung the contents of the box into the ninth tea chest, he portrayed the exact mood and demeanour of a person emptying into a dustbin the ashes from a raked out fire. He had ceased to care about the S bits which he had told me were so vital to the sleeping soldiery of Saudi Arabia.

As a precaution against a sudden reorganisation of the shop, I moved one of the tea chests with the aid of a trolley to a site closer to the beast. From here I was able to conduct my fraud in a more gentlemanly fashion. I did not have to stuff my pockets with the frenzied speed of a smash-and-grab artist, but adopted the careless saunter of a shopper, cardboard box in hand.

I changed my timetable of work. In the mornings I switched on the beast, spat on it, then disappeared to the toilets for an hour's reading. On my return I filled the out-tray cardboard box with what I deemed to be an hours produce of S bits, spat on the beast again, and disappeared for a long tea break and more reading. About ten minutes before the lunch break, and final bell, I would sit in front of the beast and bang away at the pedal as though I had been at it all day.

My output increased, and as befits an outstanding worker the foreman would sometimes stop to chat with me about the state of British industry, and allied engineering matters. He said he was really pleased at my progress.

"I can see you've really got the hang of this job," he said, digging his fingers reverentially into a box full to the brim with gleaming S bits.

"As you said," I agreed, tossing a handful over my shoulder like salt, "it takes a bit of intelligence to do this job, but I got there in the end."

Between tea breaks and toilet I managed to read Chaucer, Shakespeare, Huxley, and Emily Brontë. My secret store of S bits would take me through several workfree months, but I was just as determined to get a job on the cleaners as soon as possible. For one thing, the daily headaches were not doing me any good. I decided to get the exam off my mind before I tried out any further plans.

The Saturday before the exams when the doors were opened for the evening the Tannoy was calling, "Krishnamma to the office. Krishnamma to the office." I suffered an access of foreboding; such calls over the public address system were usually bad news.

"AG* wants to see you," the screw in the office said. He pointed with an angled forefinger towards an unmarked door.

I knocked and went in.

Peter Quinn was a tall, big-boned man with an open rustic face. He had an entanglement of dark curly hair which spilled over the sides of his head and ears. It gave him a golliwog effect. He was wearing a tweed jacket, with regulation leather patches on the elbow, and a heavy woollen scarf. There was a smell of joss stick in the room. A guitar lay across his table, and he was busy changing a string.

He got up to shake hands and motioned towards an armchair. Despite several weeks initiation into the lack of ceremony at the Lazy L, a vague, undiagnosed feeling welled up in me as I shook hands. I just wasn't ready, perhaps did not wish, to be treated with quite that degree of equality by a custodian.

"Peter Quinn. I'm the AG," he said. "And you're Krishnamma, called Kris I understand."

I nodded. "What do I call you," I asked.

"Peter is fine," he said. He had an open direct manner. He had obviously just come in, as he took his scarf and jacket off and hung them up.

I noticed his tie, and recognised it instantly. In the recognition I remembered the fastidious Anglomaniac uncle who used to wear it to social functions, and explain in elaborate detail what it signified, and why he was privileged to wear it.

"Please sit down," Peter said. "The reason I wanted to see you was just to get acquainted, and then to tell you your wife rang today to say she's coming up with the children next month to visit."

"Did you speak to her yourself?" I asked.

He told me he had, and that the ensuing conversation had established that they both belonged to the same political clique. I took note of the Manchester Guardian, and Private Eye on his desk, and guessed how that conversation may have gone. It made me feel I had been favourably introduced by Daisy. Her absence was a real presence for me in that room as we talked.

*   Assistant Governor

"Cambridge tie, Peter?" I asked.

He looked startled for a moment.

"Not many people in here recognise it," he said carefully.

I told him the story of the Uncle in India.

"I only wear it to niggle the old man," he said. He pointed to a photocopy of a photograph on the wall which showed him wearing the same tie talking to the Governor. A balloon coming out the Governor's mouth said, "You will never make Governor till you get your hair cut, Quinn."

I felt that several layers of convention had been dispensed with by my identification of his tie. The bones of my long deceased uncle could settle more comfortably. Some good had come of the tie he had worn so meticulously, and flaunted so brazenly, all his life. I wondered if his bones would remain quite so settled if he knew that it had been used by a disgraced nephew, in an English prison, to impress an Assistant Governor.

It occurred to me as I sat talking to him on subjects not normally discussed by prison official and prisoner—folk music and films, politics and sport—that if we had met outside we would have been friends. Our opinions seemed to be similar on most topics. Our wives would have known each other, and we would have visited each other's homes.

When I left Peter Quinn's office that evening I did so with a feeling of well-being. I also felt that he was well disposed towards me. My impression was that I had been fortunate to meet a prison official who was not run-of-the-mill; a man who would always give me straight answers. It was implicit that in return he would demand the same candour. He was not a fool.

It was that thought that was acting as a mental brake when I went to see him a few weeks later. Appointments to see him were quite informal; any prisoner who wanted to see him just knocked on the door and walked in. I had done that a couple of times. Once to borrow some old copies of Private Eye and once at his invitation to learn a few chords on the guitar. Each time I had stayed talking for about half an hour. He had showed interest in the exam I had taken, and had encouraged me to attempt an open university degree. A few days later he gave me the names of two other prisoners at the Lazy L who were doing OU Courses; an indication that he had not forgotten our conversation after I had left.

Now I was going to see him in a different spirit; in a mood of confrontation. My fear was that unless I presented my intention in a reasonable way I would lose his sympathy.

There was another fear. In the short while I had been at the Lazy L I had come to feel at home there. I do not mean that I could survive in it, or put up with it. I mean I felt comfortable there. It was not like being in prison after Winchester. And however much the thought intruded that it was the first step in becoming institutionalised, another more rational part of me argued that modern societies inaugurate institutionalism from the time you are born to the time you die, in schools and colleges, in churches and clubs, in the armed forces and offices, in hospitals and hospices. Indeed, it may be said that one's ability to be a compliant member of institutions is regarded as a sign of social responsibility. One is able to say, without inviting any comments about becoming institutionalised that one prefers to suffer one's illness in a certain hospital rather than another, because the staff are more friendly there, or to join a queue to die in one hospice rather than another, because there is colour TV in every room. But prison psychologists look aghast and scribble away madly when a prisoner says he enjoys his life in a certain prison. His statement is construed as a Freudian slip that indicates a predilection for prison life in general, rather than as one of preference between prison regimes. They seem unable to allow for the possibility that he may be speaking in a comparative sense, and if given wider choices he would choose somewhere without bolts and bars.

As I sat waiting to go into Peter's office I reviewed the privileges and facilities I was in danger of losing by what I proposed to do: good food, self catering arrangements, centrally heated rooms, a key to the door, the ability to move about unlocked from 7 am to 9 pm, two television and video rooms, card room, hot showers all day long, educational classes, hobbies, well equipped gymnasium, and grassy fields for exercise. One was allowed to have in one's cell a record player, radio and musical instrument, and as many books of almost any sort that you wanted. There was a good library, daily newspapers and facilities to have magazines sent in. Family and friends could visit for two hours each fortnight in a pleasant visiting room. And above all else the civility, overt good humour, and humanitarian attitude of the staff at all levels who ran the place.

As I piled up these assets and saw on the debit side a prison like Winchester with its overcrowding, twenty three hour lock-ups, one, two-minute shower a week, one, half-hour visit a month, and above all else the snarling pack of dogs who ran it, I was on the point of changing my mind, when the door opened and Peter beckoned me in.

His hands were spotted with paints of various colours. "Cottage decorating," he said.

I decided to plunge straight in and get it over with. "I've come to see you on a matter relating to a labour change," I said.

He sat down behind his desk and jotted something down. "Labour changes are not normally my department," he said, "but go on and I'll see if I can help."

"I am going to refuse to go to work on Monday and take the consequences," I said.

"What's brought this on?" he asked. He did not seem perturbed.

I told him of the labour change I had been given from one ear-splitting shop noise to another one with a different sort of membrane piercing sound. I told him I couldn't take it any more. The analogy I wanted the prison authorities to consider was that of a man who is given a hammer each morning and told to beat himself on the head with it until it produces a headache, then he is allowed to go to the doctor and get a pain-killer, then ordered to beat himself again with the hammer.

"The Penal System of Britain is not empowered to do that to a prisoner," I said, trying to give the sentence a pulpit resonance for effect.

"I would advise you against refusing labour. That sounds like an ultimatum," he began. "Now let me see," he continued, "it's too late today, but what I'll do is put out a few feelers to find out what the chances are of getting you another job. One on the cleaners, which is what I think you want. I've been here less than three months myself. So I'm quite new to this whole operation. I'd like to find out for myself how the internal politics of these labour changes work. But you will have to leave it till Thursday. If you do anything hasty before then it will definitely count against you."

So the beast and I had not parted for ever after all. On Monday I was back there to give it an early morning curse and spit. Even though the exams were over I kept my contact with the beast to a minimum. Since part of the shop was not working there were always a few men in the alcove where the tea was made reading newspapers, and generally setting the world to rights. I used to join them to debate the great issues of the 20th century, such as whether British prisons would ever allow conjugal visits, and what was to happen to guys who had no one to conjugle with.

On Tuesday, quite by chance, I discovered that Peter Quinn had gone on holiday and would not be back for a month. It was disheartening news. I reasoned that it was the end of the feelers he said he was going to put out. Thursday would come and go without any change in my circumstances, and I would have to revert to my original plan.

On Thursday evening Taff's distinctive accent came over on the Tannoy calling me to the office.

"Where is Chesapeake Bay?" he asked. There had evolved between us a quiz game based on a knowledge of world geography. We would ask each other questions about the location of a geographical feature at those times when our paths crossed, as at that moment.

"Chesapeake Bay is in America," I said.

"Not good enough," Taff said. "You have to be more specific. Where in America?"

"West coast, near California."

"You're a long way out. It's south of New York. Five four to me," he said.

The rules of the game were that the first one to reach ten got a Mars bar from the other.

"Any how that's not what I want to see you about," he said. It's about your labour change. The AG had a word with me before he went on his holiday. As it happens I've been drafted on to the allocation board. The members of the board change every three months and new officers come on to it. It's an extra duty we all have to do, besides our job on the wing. Now if you'll just be patient I'll see that you get a change of labour out of the shops."

"Out of the shops to where?" I asked.

"Yard Party," he replied. The Yard Party was the prime job for people who did not want to work in prison. I knew a man who belonged to it, and he was for ever complaining that he had to work nearly an hour a day.

I could have done a triple backward somersault of jubilation, but I was still wary.

"What does 'be patient' mean? If it means months and months of waiting ..." I left the sentence unfinished.

"Not months and months," he said, "I'm only in there three months. So, I'd say six weeks. I happen to know the requirements on the Yard party, and there are going to be a couple of vacancies on it soon.

A group of prisoners were milling around outside the office door reading some notices. Taff motioned to me to close the door. "Is it definite I'll get a job on the Yard Party in six weeks' time," I asked.

He didn't hesitate.

"It's definite," he said. "But don't broadcast it. In fact don't say anything until I give you the word. OK?"

"OK," I said.

"Another thing," he said, as I was leaving, "don't get into any trouble between now and then. You'll fuck it up if you do!"

I promised not to and left.

He was better than his estimation; at the end of three weeks he came into the Light Engineers to see me. I invited him to spit on the beast. He declined the invitation.

"It's official now. You've got the job, start Monday, but don't make too much of it or I'll have half the nick after me for jobs. And there's only so many I can help."

"So what's the capital of Paraguay?" I asked. It was an easy question, but I was feeling generous. He got it right.

The score stood at six four to him.

A couple of days after Peter Quinn got back to work I met him in the corridor.

"I'm on the Yard Party now, Peter," I said, and thanked him for the feelers he had put out.

"Don't thank me," he said, "I only learned about it this morning by looking at the Labour Board." There was an air of studied surprise on his face, and he was smiling in a knowing way.

So I thanked him again.

Consider the Career Opportunity Scheme offered to prisoners as part of the rehabilitation programme.

It is a resounding success. Daily, from the portals of British prisons, men are released, who never go back to their old criminal patterns. They have learned their lesson; changed their ways; given themselves different, loftier aspirations.

Almost exclusively the prisoners who change in this dramatic fashion, are drawn from the fraternity who have been engaged in what may be described as profitable crimes; armed robbers, drug smugglers, fences, and men convicted of fraud. It is in the hearts and minds of these worldly, sophisticated criminals that the light of reason, and regret, gets switched on.

'Never again,' says the bank robber.

'Me too,' insists the drug smuggler.

'Don't leave us out,' cry the fence and the man convicted of fraud.

'We also have seen the error of our ways. It is all going to be different when we are released. By God, you'll see.'

And so it is. Quite different. Those unversed in the recondite strategy of the careers opportunity scheme, may be alarmed to think that a constant stream of criminals in the form of plumbers, carpenters, and candlestick makers, are being released into the world outside, where these trades are over subscribed.

They need not fear. The scheme works much more discreetly. The armed robbers become drug smugglers; the drug smugglers try a bit of fraud; and the men of fraud bring their guile and polish to the business of receiving stolen property. A perfect cross pollination of disciplines, which ensures that the criminal plant is hybridized, and grows sturdier.

If any, or all of them are successful in their chosen ventures, it is a customary tradition that they toast the name of the Technical College of Crime where they learned their new craft.

Chapter 5

Having managed to get myself the job I wanted I started to take an interest in my domestic surroundings. My work as a member of the Yard Party emptying dustbins classed me as a cleaner, which meant that I had a lot of spare time on the wing.

Using the analogy of the prison as a strange country I was visiting, C wing became a town in that country; the three floors became boroughs of that town. And the individual spurs became streets in those boroughs.

My house was number 5 on the street known as Tiger Bay. At one time all seven tenants who lived there were from Wales. When I got there, and was given a lease of ten years on number 5, the residents were more cosmopolitan, but the name had stuck. Throughout the Lazy L that particular spur was known as Tiger Bay.

One of my most interesting neighbours was called Uncle George and lived in number 9 on our street.

I had met him in the first few minutes of the first day. A representative of my landlord, The Crown, had given me the key to number 5 and had just left when he came by with a jug of tea and offered me a cup.

"Where're you from?" he asked.

"India," I replied.

"Where's that? Is it a big place?" His face was straight, but I saw the glint of humour in his eyes.

I kept my face straight and pointed through the bars.

"See that high wall over there, the one everyone here would like to get over, India is just over the other side," I said.

We liked each other from that first exchange.

He was in his late fifties, comfortably retired in Spain. The reason he was at the Lazy L doing a six year sentence was because of 'a bit of work' that took place five years previously. Tracks that were not completely covered, had led back to his front door, through a circuitous route, of chance and coincidence. Even so, he felt he had had a 'result'. His peers who knew his life, and the amount of 'work' he had done, shared that opinion.

George was a big boned, heavily built man, over six feet tall, with a puckish face that smiled easily. A face that was homely, and crafty, in turn. An extrovert London humour hid a sharp perceptive intelligence. An intelligence that had helped to make him amongst the best in his business. He had been in a prison just once before for eighteen months. The amount of money earned through his activities, balanced against the time he had spent in prisons, made him a success. George's speciality was to enter the houses of the rich, tie them up, and leave with their valuables—a 'wrap up' artist.

His job on the wing was precise and easily defined. It was to brush down two flights of stairs—twenty six steps, once a day. On energetic days he mopped them. When a friend saw him actually wielding mop or broom, he would stop to hold his back.

"This work is going to be the death of me," he would say. "If I go suddenly in the night I've left you me brush and mop bucket."

Most of the time he wore dark blue overalls, with the top end tucked into his waist, which made them look like trousers. For outside use, where overalls were not permitted, he had a genuinely patched pair of jeans. On an impulse, he went to the clothing store once and got himself a new pair of 36" waist jeans. They got stuck just above his knees. "Must be a small 36," he said. The experience persuaded him to keep his old jeans, which he was on the point of dispensing with.

He was a prodigious eater, and belonged to two different food clubs, and was a visiting member in a couple of others. He carried a substantial belly to prove it.

In the early part of his six year sentence he made an important discovery: 'puff'. A lifetime of prejudice against dope, and dope smokers, was overturned, and he became, as he called himself, an aficionado. "Can't do without my sleeper at night," he said. Sometimes I would see him coming down the landing shaking his head looking worried.

"Bad news," he would say. "Very bad news."

"What's up?" someone would ask.

"Not a drop of puff anywhere. I've got two sleepers, and that's me lot. Tomorrow I'll have to sell my young body."

Our jobs made it inevitable that we spent a lot of the day on the wing together. A custom had matured between us that if one of us made a jug of tea, the other was invited for a cup. His room was less cluttered than mine and we usually ended up there, chatting about our mutual love: puff. We pooled information about which wing had the best, and how we could get hold of some.

It was at one of these chats that a chance remark with connotations of practical psychology about an incident in his life made me curious about how one of his 'bits of work' was conceived, and carried out. I had until then, a fixed notion that subtlety played no part in his profession; that force and terror were the only instruments of his accomplishment. I also wanted to justify the hopes invested in me by the authorities that safeguard law and order in the country, that while I was in prison I would not waste my time, but form new criminal interests that would help me break the law in more diverse ways next time.

He was in his favourite position, full length on the bed, propped up by two pillows. His stomach under the overalls suggested the shape of a giant turtle at rest. On a table, strategically placed, so that he did not have to move, were four bars of chocolate, a packet of Jaffa cakes and a large bag of crisps. This was his between lunch and tea snack.

"So how do you get started on one of your jobs," I asked.

"Get started?"

"I mean, obviously you don't just go to the first big house you see and rob it. Do you?"

He pulled out a ready made joint from his overall pocket and waved it in front of me grinning.

"Didn't know I had that, did you?" He lit up and leaned back against his pillows, sighing audibly.

"Usually it's all down to info received. Boozers are good places to first hear of something like that. Someone may be talking about houses in the area, or it may be the maid or au pair's boyfriend; then again it could be some one in an insurance company. They're the best. You know exactly what the prize is, and also the insurance angle could become important at the death."

"How's that?"

"If old Bill can't get the stuff back and the whole thing has died down, the insurance company will put it about through one or two faces they've worked with before, that they are willing to do a deal. Say the prize is insured with them for a hundred grand, they'd probably do a deal for twenty grand—no questions asked.

"Does that happen often?"

George rubbed a forefinger across the stubble on his chin, and took a deep toke on the joint and passed it over to me.

"Not often. But it does happen. Common sense ain't it?"

"If it's the maid's boyfriend who's giving you the information, how do you work that?"

"He never gets to see me, or us I should say. Naw, we never meet the geezer. That would be bollocks. We get the info from some one who gets to know the boyfriend. If we get the prize, we put him in for a good drink out of it. The boyfriend is probably a straight goer. It wouldn't do for him to see us."

"What sort of information do you need?"

"Everything. The more the better. We can sift through what we don't want. The more we know, the more efficient we are going to be when we go in. The kind of stuff we want to know: are there any cameras? How many people live in the gaff? When they go out? When they come in? Any kids? Bodyguard? Cook? Gardener? Where the safe is? Is it belled? Is there an extra special prize we're lookin' for? Anything like that. Once, we rung the bell, and there was a flash to our right. We look that way instinctively, and there's another one. Two photos. One head on, one profile. A camera that works off a doorbell. The cunt never told us about that. Turns out he always went to the servant's entrance, and didn't know about it."

"What did you do?"

"No problem; just carried on. Got everybody wrapped up and took the film out. No, tell a lie, that's not right, we didn't know how to get it out, so we dismantled the whole camera and took it away with us. That's the sort of out of the blue thing that can fuck everything up."

"So what's next?"

"Next is who you work with. I only work with a couple of special people. They buzz me in Spain, and either I come over here or they come over to my casa and we talk about it. The most important part of the whole business is who you work with. It's no good earning fifty million on a bit of work if it's goin' to land you in the boob, because of a mug stroke by one of the others. With us, we grew up together. We made the same mistakes together. Learned our lessons together, and luckily the mistakes we made weren't bad mistakes. See, a bit of work doesn't end the minute you've counted the money out."

"Where do you sell the stuff?"

George unwrapped a Yorkie bar and waved it at me. Before I could assess whether the gesture was an invitation to have a piece he had eaten it.

"Yeah, that's usually half sold before we go on the bit of work. We check on the buyers first. There's a couple we've done business with for over ten years."

"What kind of stuff are they looking for?"

"Jewellery, pictures but nothing special Anything very special may have to be sat on. Like, for the Mona Lisa we'd have to take ten grand. With good stuff like that the scream wouldn't be worth the agro. We've had a couple of Lowries."

"The usual rate is about a third of its value, but there's always a bit of bargaining. Money and jewellery that can be reset is best."

"Ever come across anything special, that you didn't know was there?"

George squeezed the roach into a tight pellet and flicked it through the bars behind his head.

"Anything special.... no, I don't think so." He smiled suddenly remembering something. "Not special. Unexpected, yes. Come across some dirty pictures of the lady of the house once. Unimaginable. Very rude."

"Like what?"

"See you livened up there a bit as soon as I said dirty photographs. These were diabolical. Pictures of her havin' a poop on a geezer's chest. Close up."

"What was she like?"

"Why? Somebody you know is it?"

He stopped to pull out another ready made joint from his pocket.

"The doctor has told me to take two of these white ones and four of these brown ones," he said unwrapping another Yorkie bar. He made the same half hearted movement with it in my direction but once again, before I could interpret its meaning he had swallowed it.

"I'm glad I started this diet," he said. "Feel ever so much better for it. Not easy to keep takin' these pills and medicines."

"So what did she look like?"

"About forty-five I suppose. Like a fashion-conscious forty-five year old would look. A bit hard looking. Thinks she's still got it. Good figure."

"Why would she keep photographs of herself having a crap?"

"How should I fucking know. But that's what they were.

Maybe she thought it was normal, or her bowels wouldn't work any other way. I don't know much about rude things like that."

"So what did you do with them?"

"Perfect gentleman. I kept them. But there was a bit of cleverness there. Cockney cunning see? I was in the main room layin' 'em down."

"Laying them down?"

"Yeah. They're already tied up and I'm makin' sure they didn't do anythin' silly. Her, and the maid, laid out on the carpet, hands and feet taped up. The other two were in the study with the husband or boyfriend, getting him to open the safe. One of them come back and give me this leather thing like a wallet. I could tell by the look on her face I had something; and she knew what was in the wallet. I took a quick look; saw it was her, and put it away with the negatives and all, in my pocket. This is where the cunning comes in. If I'd made a big hoot about it, shouted and joked about it, I'd have lost her."

"Lost her?" You have her tied up hand and foot, lying at your feet, with a gun in your hand. How do you mean, 'lost her'."

George gave me a disbelieving, pitying look—the sort a master of his art might give to a dumb pupil.

"Yeah, lost her. I didn't know where the lads had found it; in the safe or in her bedroom with her private things, in her jewellery box or what. She may even have had it pugged away somewhere, and the lads have found it. Don't forget, they are pros, they'd find anything pugged away. So supposin' her old man or whatever he is to her, opening the safe in the other room, doesn't know about these photos. I know it's unlikely; living in the same house together. But sometimes man and wife keep secrets from each other all their lives. So can you imagine what's going to happen? When the law get here she'll have persuaded the others to say we were black men with red hair."

"Did you say anything to her?"

"No need to. What am I, a judge? I rob people, and she shits on them. She understood the situation perfectly. It was all done without fuss. Business contract. She knew without me sayin' anythin' that if she played it our way she'd get 'em back in the post—if not they'd go to the local vicar, or whatever. Give her her due though, she just stared at me real defiant as if to say, 'So fucking what?' But it never got that far. When we had a chance to examine the photos properly it turns out the geezer she was havin' the pooh pooh on was her husband anyway. We never got a pull for it. I've always wondered how they'd box if we had been pulled."

George picked up an apple and took an awesome bite out of it. A dope-initiated hunger swept over me. I put it to him in a roundabout sort of way using such words as hospitality, and courtesy, that I would like a piece of stale bread or similar sustenance; that I was on the verge of terminal starvation.

"I suppose you want one of my chocolates," he said, tossing the apple core out of the window. A flock of feeding pigeons took off and the sound of an ovation of palms sped away, and died across the rugby fields.

He threw me a Yorkie bar, and unwrapped the last one for himself.

"Remember what you asked about finding something special. I just thought of something. I did once. A kettle, the watch of my dreams you could say. Other people dream of a Rolls Royce or whatever. It was a Cartier. Platinum with a black dial no digits. I'd love to have kept that, but see, that would have been a mug stroke. It was too distinctive—serial number and everything."

"How do you first get into the house; disguised as what?"

"Depends. You get to know your people. If it's a newly decorated house we go in as painters. Sometimes delivering flowers. Usually something that gives us a way to keep the guns hidden; like a painter's sheet or a big bunch of flowers. I've even been in as a policeman. We got false beards and wigs on and usually a cap of some sort. One thing to keep in mind is to make your talk at the door fit your clothes, in case of bugs. If we're goin' in as painters talk about paintin'."

"How much luggage do you take in?"

"All got hand guns, and definitely a sawn off. Very persuasive; shot guns. Hand guns are convenient, but a sawn off is more commanding. So many good replicas with hand guns, one of 'em might be tempted to have a go thinking it's the same as the one he saw down the supermarket. But with a sawn off there's no mistaking it's shape. Is there? Those are the main things; the rest are just bits and pieces. A bit of tape, handcuffs if you got 'em. I'm not a great one for squirt."

"Squirt?"

"Ammonia in a squeezy bottle; for the eyes, if everything goes wrong. How you go in is important. As gently as possible; must stop the involuntary scream. I always talk slowly in a low voice. The first audible word I say is 'sorry' before I show her the gun. It's usually the maid or nannie who comes to the door. I have the sawn off in a place where I can bring it round quickly."

As George spoke of guns a wavering image distracted me. I remembered the time—the only time guns had been pointed at me. When friends asked me later how I had felt; what my overriding emotion was in those first few seconds, I had to say it was not fear; just disbelief. I was able, without contrivance to transfer that feeling to the maid, wearing her opening-the-door smile, and looking down blankly at the sawn off shot gun inches from her face. This is television! This isn't happening to me! I am beginning to see how these precious few seconds, when reality is suspended, are important to the robbers.

"We don't want her screaming the gaff down before we're in. I'd have to get her round the gregory, and that's not easy when you got a gun in one hand. The other two will be coming through the door as quickly and naturally as possible. They round up the others while I hold the maid. When I say hold her, I mean I am talkin' to her all the time in a low voice with enough threat in it to keep her still, but not frighten her too much. "We don't want no screams at this point. If I think she's going to go, I whack her across the face but it's got to be done without malice, like a doctor would; one hard slap. If you make an emotional attack she will start screaming. Probably thinks you are some kind of sex maniac. See, for the time you are there, say forty-five minutes or an hour, *you are the Law*. As soon as you've established that law you've cracked it. That's where body guards can be a help sometimes."

"It's a *help* to have a body guard against you?"

"Yeah. He's a pro same as you are; less likely to give trouble than a straight goer. With us it's a clinical bit of work. And the same with him; he's doing a job, same as we are. He knows what terrible things a gun can do. SEEN what it can do, and I don't mean just on TV. We had one once who half went our way. Did most of our job for us."

"How did he do that?"

"By tellin' the others, the hostages if you like, not to do anythin' silly, and to do exactly as we asked. It's in his interest to build us up; to call us dangerous professionals. 'It's all graft for later, when the law get there. He gets the praise for bein' the hero who's saved the others from gettin' hurt. See, after it's all over, there's one thing that's going to come out, and that is that he's failed at his job. He needs all the mag he can get."

"Mag?"

"Yeah, mitigation, if he wants to keep his job. I could write out a script for him if he couldn't think of it himself. I've even took one of them aside and said, do you want us to give you a clump to help with your mag. He declined the offer. See, to cover himself, all he's got to say is something like: 'I could have made a show and maybe took a couple of them out of the game, but in the process some of the family could have been hurt'. He knows it's all covered by insurance. 'Course it don't always work that smooth. One geezer we had, half fancied his chances I suppose. We had to prove to the cunt the guns were real and loaded. I could feel we were goin' to lose him; I stuck a cushion over the gun, .38 it was, and blasted a bookcase. That quietened him right down and the others. That's the joke of it when we get billed as dangerous professionals: it ain't the pros who are the danger it's the fucking cowboys at the game who are dangerous. They crack in an' terrorise people.

"There's no need for all that. When I'm lookin' through a chest of drawers or something like that, I don't throw the gear all over the gaff. Only mugs do that. And remember all this could work for you in an I.d. I don't mean one that's straight. If she recognises you in one of those she's gonna pick you out and that's the end of it. I mean the ones that are bent; rigged up by the Old Bill. As soon as there's a tie up or robbery the Old Bill check out the people who've been robbed. Don't worry, about that. CRO[*] them to see if they can bend them. They may show them a photo of you and say, we know that's him, now go down the line and pick him out. Most straight goers; eight out of ten I should say, don't want to think the robbers are goin' to get away with it. So they pick you out. End of story. But see, if you'd behaved half decently while you was in there robbin' them, not needlessly ill-treated them, I reckon they're less likely to fall in with all the law tell 'em. They are less likely to become dishonest and pick out a man they didn't themselves recognise. It's never got that far on the bits of work I've been on, so I don't know if it works that way; but it's a bit of insurance; it doesn't hurt anyway. It's nice to be nice. You'd be amazed at the rapport you can get going with them sometimes.

"The only place you could get hiccoughs is getting the man to open the safe or whatever. Here again you want to leave him his dignity. If you threaten to kick the shit out of him if he doesn't open up you may be creating a resistance where truthfully there was none. You say to him; look if you're goin' to be silly about this, it won't be you who gets hurt; it'll be your wife and kid. And you make sure you say it so as they can all hear it. You are there to rob him of his money and jewels, not his manhood. This way you let him keep that. At the post-mortem after we've gone he comes out with his dignity. It doesn't look as though he's shit himself and opened the safe; he's done what any man would do when his wife and kid are bein' threatened. You learn a lot about people of that class if you like.

"We went in this house once and there was this ugly Paddy bird, scullery maid or whatever; not upstairs quality. Very definitely downstairs material. Small dumpy woman, frizzy hair, big red hands, y'know the type. She went completely to pieces; sobbing, crying, hysterical. You should've seen the way the others treated her. I don't mean us lot. I mean the people she was workin' for. They couldn't forget the class difference even then when they was all in the same boat, tied up. There was a man, woman and teenage daughter, and they was all takin' it out of the Paddy. Sayin' things like 'Do stop snivelling, Bridget'." (George mimicked the tones of that social group.) "I felt sorry for her in the end. She was sobbin' away that her hands hurt. In the end I cut the tape away; she had her

[*] Criminal Register Office

45

hands behind her back. I remember rubbing her wrists and tyin' her hands in front of her loosely. The way she looked at me you'd a thought I was Paul Newman."

George sat up suddenly, taking deep breaths, gasping, rubbing his chest. "Keep gettin' a tight feeling 'cross here." He looked concerned for a second but it was momentary.

"Reckon it's overtraining," he said. "Top athletes go like that, get sudden twinges. Think I'll give the gym a miss for a few days."

George's only visits to the gym were on Saturdays when it was used as a cinema, and his sporting contacts amounted to shouting obscenities at the rugby players, with a group of like-minded connoisseurs of the game.

"Are you all right?" I asked.

"I think I'd feel a lot better if I had a couple of these pills," he said, opening a packet of Jaffa cakes. He ate two and lay back clutching the packet to his bosom. There was no danger of being offered any.

"Would you hurt somebody; I mean torture them to open the safe?"

"Of course. If you're not willing to do that you ain't entitled to be there. This is a hard thing to say, but the prize is everything. You got to think that way. No good being half-hearted about it. I know geezers who put rice in the cartridges. That's bollocks. Where are they going? A wedding!"

"What about children?"

"What about children?"

"Would you hurt them?"

He slipped another couple of Jaffa cakes out of the packet and studied the ceiling as though some edict on morality or conscience that appertained to people of his chosen profession might be inscribed there.

"No. There's never any need to do that. That's where acid is such a lovely thing to have. Separate the child from the parents, and threaten them that they open up or the child gets it. First you show 'em what it can do. Pour a bit on a table or whatever: Once it starts to blister the wood they're ready to do anything. The unuttered threat is always more persuasive. It never comes to hurting the child. If the *threat* of doing the kid ain't enough they're selfish people. There's only one thing to do to them sort of people. Do *them* with the acid. Them sort might have the nerve to let their child suffer, but couldn't stand it themselves. If it really got that far I'd do them somewhere it doesn't show, like on the thigh or whatever, an' tell 'em the next lots on their face. Talkin' about children. We was in this house once, and when the child come in from school she run straight to her mum.

Not the nannie or the father. As soon as we saw that, we knew we had cracked it. We had the key. This was a mum not a mother. She'd do anythin' to stop her child bein' hurt. There's always something that shows you how to box."

"But people do get hurt sometimes?"

"'Course; that happens sometimes. It's part of the game We're lookin' at what? Ten maybe fifteen years if we get captured. We ain't wipin' our mouth at the first bit of ag. But you can be sure that if we did pull the trigger it would be the last resort. We would have tried everything else first.

No, I mean the mugs who don't plan enough. Got no sympathy for them. Most of the time people get hurt or killed because of accidents—because they're so fucking nervous. Not worth that" (George made the motions of a man masturbating; a derisive dismissal of their aspirations to be armed robbers).

"I check and recheck everything, especially the guns. They're the tools of your trade." His voice changed from the confident tones of exposition to an almost reverential one as he spoke the words 'tools of your trade'.

"I know a bloke, layin' 'em down, gets a bit of lip from one of the geezers and goes to prod him in the back of the neck and the gun goes off. How'd you make that out? It's no good sayin' the trigger was faulty, or whatever. He wasn't entitled to handle a gun if he didn't know all about it *before* he went on the bit of work."

"What happened to him?"

"To who?"

"The guy who got shot?"

George looked at me in amazement. "Whadd'ya think happened. Point blank behind the head. Are you kiddin'? The bloke who done it is here." He mentioned a name. I realised I had played badminton with him a couple of times. He was doing a recommended twenty five years of a life sentence. "The more the violence the bigger the scream from the papers and television. A couple of blokes had to go missing after that bit of work, who weren't even on it. They were in that area at the time, and knew they'd get a pull. See how their mistakes involve other people. Mugs. This is what I was sayin' earlier. You got to know the people you're workin' with. I've backed bits of work because the bloke who gave us the info wanted to come on it."

George made violent movements with his hands and feet as though he was using a rowing machine. Having observed these movements on previous occasions, I knew he was trying to get up. A massive effort failed, and he fell back. A second more determined one saw him upright.

"Still have the old acrobatic movements," he said modestly.

He put his slippers on and walked away in the direction of the toilets.

On his return, as though other memories of the old days had been reactivated, he started speaking before he had sat down.

"Even when we're coming out, we always say something like see you later or something, as though we're talkin' to somebody in the house. Just in case there's a nosy neighbour who we can't see watching us. It's that sort of small thing that could become crucial later on. See, here's a thing: I always like to walk down the road the house is on, to get a feel of it. I know it's a silly point, but you feel less of a stranger. There's all sorts of small things you learn as you go along."

"Like what?"

"Like.... from the top of my head, tell me, how would you open a chest of drawers if you're in a hurry. You don't know, do you?"

My mind was beginning to adjust to the problem as George spoke.

"Always start with the bottom drawer first. That way you don't have to keep closing them to get to the next one."

"So how did it go wrong for you this time?"

"It didn't."

"But you're here."

"Am I?" George looked disbelievingly around. He felt his arms and legs and patted his stomach, and remembering that it had not been fed for a while, slipped a couple of Jaffa cakes down his throat. "Good God: so I am. How long have I been here? Thought I was on the Costa Blanca. 'Course I'm fucking here, but it ain't for any of the bits of work I been on. I could have got fourteen years for any of those. No, this was because of the aftermath on a bit of work. Insurance that went wrong."

"Insurance?"

"Yeah. You got to treat it as a trade. If you're a window cleaner you must look to the day you fall off your ladder, and plan for that day. I'd be dreamin' if I didn't think I'd get a pull now and again. It's only natural.

Part of the game. Even if you're nicked for a bit of work, it's not the end of the world. There's ways you can box there, so long as you ain't hung yourself already. I reckon ninety per cent, no ninety eight per cent of blokes who get bird, get it for what they've said in those first forty eight hours in the police cells. They put themselves in it. I say nothing at all. I mean anythin'. No matter how silly the question is. Like 'Do you play golf' or whatever. Say nothing. Forty eight hours later you're either nicked or in the boozer. If you're on remand you got time to quieten down and plan how to box.

"It's not nice for anyone, I don't care who it is, to get picked off the street and put in a police cell. You're at your lowest ebb then. But you should've thought about this as though it was definitely going to happen. Not be unprepared and scrabble around in a panic."

"How many times have you been charged?"

"Loads of times. No that's not right. Six times."

"And?"

"Nothin'. Got off. Two got slung out before committal. Over a year on remand on one of the others and got a not guilty. One, we got hold of the jury. That's the sort of thing the ordinary thief doesn't think about till it's too late. You know beforehand, who to see if the jury has to be got at. But you must leave it to the experts. That's why I'm here now. Because I went out of my field. Tryin' to pervert the course of justice. I've 'ad a couple of trades with Old Bill. How to go about that is good info to have. Best is if you can do the deal in the street away from the station. Another way with Old Bill is gettin' bail. See, bail in itself ain't worth that (rapid masturbatory handshaking) but while you're out you can get your act together and come in strong at court. Alibis and that sort of thing. We've had some good results. We were on the book* once and gettin' the full treatment bein' taken to court. You know what I mean dontcha? Police car front and back; three motor bikes and a chopper. Armed police escortin' us, sirens going, no stopping for lights. You'd a thought it was the Third World War startin'.

"Get to court and ten minutes later we was signin' our bail papers. See *they* don't give you bail, but they could make their objections so weak or silly that a good brief has no problems. The other way is with the actual offence. This is in court. Right? Get them to fuck the case up. Get it into them to make a big thing about July the 14th. The day you was havin' tea with the vicar and fifty guests. Their briefs will build most of the evidence around that date. When that is shot down the rest should fall with it. I say should but it doesn't have to. Old Bill still got to be paid. They done their bit, but a bad judge can swing it the other way. Touch wood. I've been lucky. That's the reason I give it all up. The last time was too close for comfort. That's it for me. As soon as this one's out the way I'm back to my house and swimming pool; round of golf, go fishing take my granddaughter to the village for an ice cream."

* Category A prisoners who are guarded more securely. Each has a book in which pertinent details are kept.

George nudged the framed photograph of a chubby little girl with pink balloon cheeks and a mischievous smile. It was the only photograph he had in the room. It was very special.

The question formed itself.

"What would you do if it happened to you?"

"You mean if three geezers come in to my place with guns?"

"Yes.

"No problem at all. I think I'd be the best robberee (good word that ain't it) they ever had. I'd help them all I could. There y'are mate, safe over there. Here's the combination, or key or whatever. I'll rip the phone out. No need to make a mess. Take what you want. Drinks over there. Goodbye. See you later."

When I left George that afternoon, he was opening a packet of crisps and looking around feverishly for something else to eat.

I was late for work and the screw was petulant.

"Where have you been?" he asked.

"Terribly sorry orificer," I said. "I was just finishing off a lesson in behavioural psychology."

"What the fuck's that? Anyway, gimme one of those chocolates you're eating."

He was a pleasant man who had taken our party out before, and his annoyance at my lateness was feigned. We set off through the double doors at the centre, towards the furnace where the green goddess was parked.

In my head concepts and symbols quarelled and would not make peace. A lovely bottle of acid was jostled out of focus by a scarred and blinded face. My notion of a workmen's compendium of tools has a new addition; it has amputated nostrils of black steel and a wooden stock. A jovial man, retired in the sun, takes his granddaughter to the shops. They walk hand in hand, he makes faces and funny noises to set her laughing. She will remember her granddaddy as a man of kindness and softness. A stranger obliterates that picture. A man in painters' overalls. There is a chilling menace in all his movements. The mother who faces him will remember for ever the cold eyes that wandered from the bottle in his hand to her little boy.

Somehow all these features assimilate a little of each other's contours, and form the texture of his life. I know they do, but I don't know how.

What I do know is that the next time I have a need to open a chest of drawers in a hurry, I will start at the bottom.

The cliché so often used by the media, "ROTTING AWAY IN JAIL", is not entirely accurate. Some of those undergoing long periods of incarceration throw themselves vigorously into academic endeavour. Some make physical fitness their goal, the gym their shrine. Yet others, depending on the nature of the individual, find more diverse ways to maintain growth in their lives...

Joe looked strained. There was about him an air of determined concentration; as well there should be.

He was standing in a patch of segmented sunshine that streamed in through the bars of the laundry gate. It was an area crowded with derelict washing machines, and other junk. Here, off duty laundry workers spent their leisure moments. Joe was counting, slowly, painfully.

The bookie was taking bets; two guys were playing crib; and the Tanzanian was giving a lecture on the correct etiquette to be observed when hijacking an aeroplane; he had qualifications to be doing so. At present he was being restrained for nine years from hijacking anything else.

Joe was standing apart, behind two waist high machines, so that from the pavement only the top half of him was visible. I walked up to the bars, and peeked over the top. There was a startling reason for the arithmetic.

He had no clothes on from the waist down—and hanging from his strangulated penis through the assistance of a device like a thick watch strap, there hung a laundry bag full of batteries of assorted sizes. It was the completed swings of the bag, back and forth, back and forth, that he was counting.

'Fourteeeen, fifteeeen, sixteeeen,' he counted through gritted teeth.

'Excuse me,' I began, 'are you sure about this?'

'Piss off,' he grunted.

I had to approach the matter in a more guileful way.

'Excuse me,' I began again, 'I don't mean to interrupt

your yoga sessions, but does that contraption really work? Is it a British patent?'

He stopped the swing of the pendulum by sitting down with extreme care on a laundry box.

'Does it work? Ha!' he laughed weakly. ''Course it bloody works, do you think I'm stupid or what? Do you think I'd be standing 'ere with these batteries 'angin' off the end of me prick, if it didn't work. Now would I?'

'Could I possibly,' I ventured, 'I mean ah, that is to say ah, or to put it another way, borrow that device for a night. I'd like to study the design, for academic reasons, you understand.'

'Piss off. You're not 'avin' laundry equipment. Make your own.'

'I don't know how.'

'Tough! See the Welfare Officer in the morning.'

With that, he disengaged himself from the watch strap, gingerly pulled his underpants over his contused penis, and with part of his equipment tucked protectively under his arm, and the other part safely inside his trousers, wandered off, whistling.

When the rest of the yard party joined me, I told them what I had seen. They didn't believe me. Nobody did. I hardly believed myself.

The truth of what I had seen was established a few weeks later, when a careless practitioner of Joe's device, someone who hadn't adjusted the watch strap just so, was taken to hospital, cursing the inventor in a high-pitched squeaky voice.

At that stage, the PEG, acronym for Penis Enlargement Gadget, was brought back to the drawing board by the anxious inventor. He said he was working on a fail safe mechanism to incorporate into his creation.

Chapter 6

In terms of time off to pursue one's own objectives the Yard Party
was precisely the job for me. When I joined it there were five others.
The six of us had to empty a total of about twenty dustbins a day into
our dustcart, called the green goddess, as a result of an accident with
a large tin of green paint that had burst, and dribbled its contents
down one side. From there it was a leisurely trot, taking it in turns to
push and pull the green goddess to the furnace.

Our leader, who traditionally acquired that position by being the
longest serving member of the party was a calamity-prone Irishman.
He was a short powerfully built man, swathed in muscles, whose
cannon ball-shaped, close-cropped head seemed to sit directly on his
shoulders with no neck to speak of. When he was pulling the green
goddess the rest of us had to act as a brake; left to drive the cart on
his own he was in danger of pulling it straight through the perimeter
wall, such was his lack of direction and coordination.

There were rumours and innuendos afloat in the prison that he
had been excommunicated from the IRA. It seems that given the job
of moving some bombs from one part of a warehouse to another he
had blown up his own people: twice. Typically, when he was caught
the English had put him in prison for fifteen years instead of gar-
landing him with medals.

His temper like his stature was short, so no one mentioned bombs
or other explosive devices when he was within earshot. When the
brake effect exerted by the rest of us was not strong enough he was
in the habit of taking the cart round corners so fast that it used to
turn over and deposit the contents of several bins in the road. He was
in his element then, spade in hand, shovelling it up and roaring his
head off laughing, blaming the rest of us for having turned the cart
over.

It took the six of us about an hour, if we worked slowly, stopping to
chat and have a cup of tea with the furnace operator, to do the work.
Soon after I joined the party there was an influx of prisoners from
another prison that had been destroyed in a riot, and the Yard Party
was increased to ten members. The officers taking the party on their
rounds, complained that they found ten members too large a group
to supervise. So the party was split into two shifts. I opted for the

afternoon shift which meant that I was back on the wing within half an hour. The rest of the day was my own.

I started a systematic attack on my weight and fitness problem. The weight was easily quantified; I had to lose about thirty pounds. The journey back to fitness was not so easy to define. I had done no physical exercise for fifteen years. My standard of physical fitness was hinted at in laboured breaths at the least exertion, and by ominous giddy turns when I stood up too fast. I had ignored their message, persuading myself that I could not spare the time. Now my time had been given back to me. It was time to begin.

I started using the gymnasium with desperate middle-aged urgency. The back room, windowless, heavy with the smell of sweat, and resonant to the sound of grunts and groans, became my place of self-inflicted torture, first for an hour, then for two hours each day. Having given me a simple circuit test which entailed going round in a circle three times doing a few knee bends, sit-ups, and picking up and putting down a few light weights, and which I failed to complete one round of, the senior PEI, Malcolm, a man with a fearsome reputation as a rugby player, had given me a simple routine of exercises to accomplish. There were a set of sit-ups, followed by skipping, and short periods on the rowing and bicycle machines.

The first month was hard, painful, and lonely in that crowded room, where groups of men in twos and threes were doing individual work-outs, and hardly spoke to each other, let alone to strangers. But slowly as the days wore on and I showed no signs of giving up, they began to greet me—recognising in the agonised expressions I wore; in the gulps of fetid air I gratefully swallowed, a fellow traveller, just starting out on a road that had once been familiar to them. Some of them stopped to give me words of advice on how best I could torture myself further. Their attitude was patronising but friendly.

Gradually I became aware of my involvement in the mood and vibrations of that sweatbox. It was then that the spirit of the room in general could affect one's own performance. It was as though we were all in the same tug-of-war team; pulling individually but to a common end. If the sounds from the speedball were rhythmic and easy; if the man next to me was doing his sit-ups without strain; if there was a distinguishable pulse to the cluster of punches on the heavy bag—then my exercises seemed less arduous. But if the speedball stuttered, or the man next to me stopped abruptly holding his back, the strength and the will drained away from me and it became a struggle.

There was another, less obvious bond, that united the members who day after day withstood the suffocating effect of that airless dungeon. We were all paying off our insurance premiums; but the policy was one that no ordinary insurance company would countenance, and the method of payment was in torn muscles, sweat, and strain. By going to that room every day we were hoping to nullify, or certainly lessen, the corrosive effects of time. Men sentenced to ten, fifteen, or twenty years imprisonment would much rather go out dead, than old and weak. Trying to ward off old age is not particular to prisoners, but there is more evident desperation about the way in which prisoners turn to exercise as a means to it in prisons. And the insurance policy is cashed when a visiting friend or relative says, "Well, look at you, so fit and well, the years have hardly touched you at all."

So I plodded on, puffing and panting, and cheating more than once. After three months I went back to try Malcolm's circuit test, and this time managed to complete all three rounds, but I was exhausted at the end of it. It was however a great improvement. After another three months in the back room I could do the circuit quite comfortably. As I became more proficient at the exercises I found them increasingly more boring. I needed to do something with a competitive edge to it. I turned to badminton.

Since I worked in the afternoons I was allowed to use the gym in the mornings. A group of about six were regular badminton players and I joined them. My first game was a revelation. I thought I was reasonably fit but I found out differently. It was much more strenuous than it looked. Half way through the set my breath came in painful jerks, and I felt nauseous. I had to concede the game and come off the court.

The next day my body ached but unlike the distaste the thought of going to the back room brought on, I could not wait to get down to play another game. And that was it. I was hooked; I became an addict. It took on the qualities of an obsession; I spent every minute I was allowed to in the gymnasium playing badminton. It was no longer a matter of insurance; I was doing it for pleasure. The fitness that derived from it was incidental. Prisons are ideal locations to have such obsessions, if one is allowed to fulfil them.

By the end of the first year at the Lazy L I could give most of the players there a good game, although there were several who could still beat me. My fitness improved from week to week, and my weight settled at an optimum level. The day I could get through a whole set without stopping was a milestone. Then it was two, and then three. I reached the stage when I could play five sets of strenuous badminton and not feel utterly drained, just pleasantly tired.

When one of the junior PEIs, himself a county-standard badminton player, started giving badminton lessons, I was the first to join. He brought in some textbooks on badminton, and in the study and execution of their contents I began to learn the game all over again; the bad habits I had acquired through just trying to win points were eradicated. I began to understand the game in much the same way as a person learning a new language may one day see past the tourist words and phrases, to the heart of the language, and grasp its idiom. I understood in practical terms what could, and could not, be done with the shuttlecock; how a game where the object was always struck in the air differed from one with ground shots. I got used to the explosive starts, sudden changes of direction, and special flexibility the game demands. I practised for hours the technique of executing drop shots, and smashing, with the same body posture.

The day I managed to win a set against the PEI I went back to the wing feeling ten foot tall. The years dwindled away and I felt half my age.

Other areas of my life were proving just as satisfactory. In fact, the first eighteen months of my incarceration at the Lazy L passed so smoothly, with no startling episodes, that as is the case with such periods of one's life, it was difficult to remember what did happen. Reference to some documents of that time confirms that I achieved a grade C pass in the GCE A level English Literature exam; not the best of grades but I was gratified that I had passed. I had also begun Spanish classes and was making modest progress there. My musical talent with the guitar was proving hard to find, but I was still looking.

During this period Daisy brought the children to visit me three times. We had agreed that the arduous day-long journey from the Isle of Wight, and the expense of bringing four children with her, could only be undertaken once every six months. On the last occasion I had seen her, it had been a heartening visit. All the children were looking well, and doing well at school. She had been given a backdated pay rise, and a tax rebate as well. There had been presents all round for the children, and a shiny new badminton racquet for me. At the end of the visit I had hugged and kissed them all, and said softly with conviction, "It's all down hill now, if I don't get parole this time, I'll get it the next. I'll be home inside two years. You'll see!"

Prophecies like that can sometimes haunt you for the rest of your life, like the phrases of a popular tune they can echo in your ears at the oddest moments; either because they turned out to be so accurate, or because they were so presumptuous. Long after the prison days were over, and the other days of my life had begun, and probably for the rest of my days anywhere, whenever I hear or have occasion to say the words, 'all downhill' I am at once transported to that visiting room of plastic-topped tables, and discreet camera surveillance.

I remember also that in those early days the street called Tiger Bay in which I had house number 5, was a neighbourhood of peace and quiet. It was an area of low profiles, and deep, untroubled sleep. There should have been, like all the other spurs, eight residences on our street, but because three of them were taken up as temporary clothing stores, there were only five.

One day Uncle George who was not the regular cleaner, but a 'sort of extra cleaner', a euphemism for unemployed person, was approached indirectly, and hesitantly asked if he would very kindly give the regular cleaner a hand, to convert one of the storerooms into an extra cell for somebody arriving the next day. After considerable grumbling about the state of his health, and that his back should not be subjected to such strain, and the amount of work he was already doing, he agreed. Uncle George was the most well informed prisoner about the internal affairs of the wing; he had a knack of wheedling information out of the screws in the guise of humorous exchanges.

"Ho! Ho!" he said, after he had done the room, or rather stood in an advisory capacity close by, while the regular cleaner did it, "mark my words, the screws are going to be like flies around shit down this spur when the new bloke gets in. Hide everything, my children, the end is upon us. I'm glad I'm gettin' out of here before the fireworks start."

George was due to be released from prison in a month's time. It wasn't quite that bad, but we had an inkling of what he meant after Barry Goodwin had been in Tiger Bay for a few weeks.

Part of Barry's personality was worn on his trousers and denim jacket—bright yellow flashes that made him stand out like a daffodil in a bed of violets. In the grading of prisoners, the dozen or so E men at the Lazy L were the most visible group.

These were the prisoners that the prison authorities deemed to be escape risks, and as a mark of that supposed capability they were compelled to wear clothes with the yellow stripes down the sides. Having to wear those flashes was called being 'put in patches'. Quite naturally, it was a status symbol to be thought of as a daring escape artist. To be awarded a set of patches a prisoner had to try to escape from the prison he was in, or, by previously having done so from another, or, by being in the opinion of the Home Office a person with enough muscle on the outside to organise an escape.

Being an E man curtails such freedom as is allowed in prisons even further. Outside their own wings they are escorted whereever they go in the prison by a screw who carries a small, black, passport-sized book, and two-way radio. The book contains his photographs (head on and sideways), his description, his wing, cell number, and where he works in the prison. After he is escorted, say to the gymnasium, the screw hands the book over to another screw who signs for it; this procedure is repeated for all his movements from one area of the prison to another, until he is back within the jurisdiction of his own wing.

At night, before the final lockup he has to put all his clothes, plastic knife, fork, and spoon, razor, and shoes, into a cardboard box, and leave them outside his door. He is left with only his underwear and bedclothes. A dim red light is left switched on all night in the cell, and an SW (special watch) sign is hung on his door handle. A screw comes around at intervals of about one hour to check through the spyhole to see that he is still there.

Having a visit is a heavily censored, public affair. The screw with the book sits a few feet away; almost a part of the conversation.

Sometimes the visit is closed, which means there is a glass barrier between the prisoner and his visitor. It is a regime that leads to a lot of tension, and frayed nerves.

The only redeeming feature of this life is that in a crowded prison an E man does not have to wait or queue for anything. If there is a line of prisoners waiting to see the doctor, the screw carrying the little black book pushes past them to the front, and the E man goes in next.

At regular intervals the authorities meet to decide whether the yellow stripes can come off the prisoner's clothes, and he can join the less supervised members of the prison community. It is not surprising that most prisoners who are put in patches look forward to the day when they are allowed out of them to join the mainstream.

Barry belonged to this category of prisoner when he first came to live in Tiger Bay. He was an Australian, and although constant association with Londoners in prison had eroded the original accent, it was still discernible now and again. He was of average height, lean and athletic, with short, dark, wiry hair, and a swarthy skin which gave him a Mediterranean appearance. His features were small, cleanly defined and well balanced. Sometimes he was brash and offensively arrogant, exuding an air of self confidence even when he, and everyone else around him, knew he had lost control of the situation. He had been in all of the punishment blocks of the dozen or so prisons that he had been held in, and waved that fact like a heraldic banner in front of him, whenever he could.

The five of us who were resident in Tiger Bay had all come to terms with our sentences, and found our niches in prison society. Such fight or defiance as some of us had once possessed had mellowed into an acceptance that of all the prisons we had been put in, the Lazy L was the best. Ironically, we had not been tamed by the harshness of regimes like Winchester, but by the Lazy L carrot of permissiveness, and unprisonlike civility. We were all marking time, reasonably contented with the minor highlights of our lives, each with our own projects to fill the months and years ahead.

Barry had never allowed himself to succumb to such feelings. To him a prison was a prison was a prison. He regarded the good ones and the bad ones, the brutal and the humane, with equal hostility, and detestation. "You guys are all institutionalised. They've broken you," is how he put it.

He had started his prison career for being part of an organised Australian shop-lifting gang. He got six years for that. His life in patches was brought on when he escaped from HMP Chelmsford. The day after his escape, so the story goes, the prisoners in Chelmsford at breakfast time, burst into a prearranged chorus of, 'Tie me kangaroo down sport'. The screws had taken the joke well, but predicted that his absence was temporary, and that he would be back.

A year or so later their retort became fact. Barry was recaptured, and faced further charges for armed robbery. This time he was given an eight year sentence. A total of fourteen years.

When he was moved to the Lazy L he was into his ninth consecutive year in prison. He had lost three years remission for taking part in riots, and burning a workshop down in HMP Hull.

The continued changes of environment that he was subjected to, were to ensure that he could not get settled in any one place, to cause, or take part in, any organised action. It was generally agreed that he had been transferred to the Lazy L, so that he could coast down the last bit of his sentence in an atmosphere that was less oppressive than he was normally used to. It was a gesture of appeasement, and at the same time for someone like Barry a slap in the face. They were telling him in effect that they had emasculated him; that they no longer considered him a dangerous and resourceful criminal.

As though in reply to that assumption in the early hours of one night soon after he arrived, the residents of Tiger Bay were awakened suddenly. There was a sound of running feet going past my door to Barry's cell. It was unknown for groups of screws to be on the landing after 9 pm. After that time, it was just the swivelling cameras that scanned the landings, and central areas. A sudden commotion at that time was as unnerving as a scream in the night, whose source, and reason, are hidden from you. The running feet changed to purposeful marching, and Barry was taken down to the punishment block. It left the rest of us in Tiger Bay clutching our bits of illegal substances to our chests like protective mothers. We fell asleep uneasily, wondering what it was all about, and if the trouble included us in any way.

He was back in circulation the next day, smiling his desperado's smile, and looking unabashed. He had been trying, he said, to unscrew the cover plate of the electronic console by the side of the door. He had had a sudden urge to find out whether what he was told at his induction, that trying to interfere with the electronics of the cell would immediately trigger an alarm in the central office, which would also indicate where it had been activated.

No material damage had been done—in fact he had not managed to get this cover plate right off, and after a check by a couple of engineers, he was given a caution, and allowed back into the same room.

As ever his breezy air of being master of all situations camouflaged the escapade to reflect some purpose for what he had done. "Took the cunts four minutes twenty three seconds to get to me," he said, smiling significantly, as though the exact time down to the last second (as in great escape stories) was somehow important, as one part of some greater plan in which such times were crucial. He inferred that even being taken down the block was part of the plan.

In any other prison such an episode would have resulted in a loss of remission, especially as it was a matter that concerned the security aspect of the prison. At the Lazy L the whole affair was not only ignored, but the authorities delivered yet another slap in the face to Barry's ego: they took him off patches. The great escaper was reduced in rank to an ordinary B category prisoner like the rest of us.

We became apprehensive in Tiger Bay; this was entirely the wrong psychology to use for someone like Barry, we thought. He would now try to prove that he was not a spent force. And in doing something reckless he would focus attention on the whole neighbourhood. We braced ourselves for the fireworks Uncle George had predicted. Fortunately for Tiger Bay that prediction did not come true. It was prevented by an unusual relationship that developed between Barry and the prisoner who took over the cell Uncle George had vacated. The new arrival in some inexplicable way, none of us could understand, had a calming effect on Barry and made him a conformist member of Tiger Bay.

Chapter 7

The new man was from Pakistan. Some of his name was Sheikh Humayune Badur; there were other bits and pieces of his name squashed on his cell card which were indecipherable. From the first day he was known simply as The Sheikh. He was about six foot tall, well padded around the stomach, and shoulders, and had a hooked nose, and hawk eyes. His moustache was thick and black, and trained to curl upwards in arrow shapes, in what used to be a popular style for the bad guys in Indian movies. It gave him a sinister, intriguing appearance, that belied his true nature.

His father had been in the diplomatic service in several Western capitals and as a result The Sheikh had been to school in England, and then majored in Business Management at an American University, before going back to Pakistan to take his place in the family textile business.

A heated argument in a public place, in which he favoured the wrong side, (Bhutto's) put him out of favour with the military government of Pakistan and he was put in prison. Massive, and judiciously placed bribes got him out within a week. After his release he was advised to leave the country as his welfare was not assured there. He left in a well planned flight, ostensibly going on a business trip abroad, but with the secret intention of not returning until there was a change in the political climate.

His long term aim had been to set up a company in London to import the textiles made by his family firm, run by relatives who had stayed out of politics. He came to London with assets of half a million pounds in bank drafts, and foreign currency.

Although he had lived in England before as a boy, it was in the protective custody of a public school. All his life he had been dependent on his family, and was expected to fill a prepared position in the traditional family business.

In London he rented an expensive apartment in the west end, and set out to discover his newly adopted home town. In that quest he discovered himself. It was the full realisation of that revelation that made him say to those of us who got to know him at the Lazy L, "You see, gentlemen, I am a compulsive gambler. An addict. It is a disease with me. One that I did not know I suffered from until I came to London."

Within two years he had lost all the money entrusted to him; various London casinos benefited. To recoup his losses he arranged for a shipment of cannabis to be sent over hidden in onyx artifacts.

He was doing an eight year sentence. He spoke English faultlessly and slowly, it was as though he was savouring the texture and flavour of each word. It gave him a learned, academic, intonation, even when he was talking about every day events. His accent was posh, public school, but now and again an Americanism—'you better believe it', reminded the listener of his college days in California.

At other times his speech reminded me of someone else in another time, and place, but I could not remember who, or where. Then listening to him one day talking about some inconsequential matter about his homeland it dawned on me. This is the speech affectation that is traditional among Indian army officers; they still talk like that to this day. It is the residual effect left behind by their erstwhile commanders. Sentences like "come on chaps, let's give it a bash"; words that have been pushed into the background of common usage like 'chum' and phrases like 'rum bird' or 'I say', appeared in his speech, giving me sudden jolts of nostalgia for a group of people who had once been familiar to me in the old country, where colloquial English of an older form is still preserved. Old, retired officers of the Raj who go back for a visit become sentimental, and wistful, to see how well their conventions have been maintained.

In everything he said or did The Sheikh exhibited an air of helpless entrenchment in a way of life that has ceased to exist here, but which is very much the norm among some sections of society in the Indian sub continent. The concept of a clutch of servants to do his every bidding, was not something to be imagined. It had been a necessity The Sheikh took for granted.

Even on his last journey to England he brought with him an old family retainer whom he described as "my personal man servant". Recognising his background and knowing it was authentic I was able to sympathise with the culture shock he was suffering from.

To the others in Tiger Bay The Sheikh was an enigma. They had never come across a Pakistani like him before. He broke all their rules of type casting.

Prisoners from Asia have, generally speaking, a good track record for toeing the line in an orderly fashion in prison. Once they are in, they tend to form small cliques, speak the language that comes most easily to them, work hard, and have a reputation for culinary skills;

an asset that makes them sought after by the screws in charge of the kitchen. Some screws as a matter of preference recruit as many Asian prisoners into their units or places of work as they can, because they know they are easy to manage, and uncomplaining.

By contrast the Sheikh's manner on first impressions was haughty, almost patronising. His absolute command of English and understanding of western culture did not limit his friends and associates to the same restricted circle as his compatriots. His culinary skills were non-existent. Asked once if he could remember any easy recipes for a good curry, he said he knew it had something to do with chopping the onions very finely. "After that you just put all the ingredients in a large kitchen utensil and cook it for a very long time," he said vaguely, twirling his moustache.

When pressed for more details, such as the names of the ingredients he became impatient. "Back home, such matters are dealt with by the women in the household or servants," he said.

Despite his warlike appearance The Sheikh was a passive, philosophical man. After a short while in the Light Engineers, he applied for a job in the clothing exchange store. It turned out to be a most fortuitous application. The officer in charge of the department had for a long time nursed the desire to learn about the stock market, and the mechanics of buying and selling shares. When he interviewed The Sheikh he discovered that chance had sent him a captive tutor. He got the job.

There were three prisoners working in the store. In no time at all the other two guys were doing all the work while The Sheikh spent his time in the back office with the screw poring over the Financial Times and several wall charts he had drawn up to better instruct his pupil.

"I'm trying to get the old duffer to invest some hard cash," The Sheikh said to us in Tiger Bay.

When the screw finally took the plunge and invested a nest egg of two thousand pounds under The Sheikh's guidance, and it showed a profit of sixty six pounds at the end of a month, The Sheikh's reputation as a financial wizard was established. Other screws heard about it, and soon the back office became a place from where there were to be heard snatches of conversation about the relative merits of different unit trusts, and futures, and commodities; at the front counter the other two struggled manfully to keep the department credible, changing shoes, and overalls, and jeans.

I went in once when The Sheikh was well established as the number one in the department, to change a pair of boots. I asked one of the guys if The Sheik was in. I was told I could not see him unless I had an appointment. It was said humorously, but I detected a trace of bitterness. Just then The Sheikh came out of the back office and seeing me came over to find out what I was there for. I told him.

"No problem," he said. "Just a minor matter. One of my chaps here will attend to your needs." He sauntered away with a preoccupied nod in their direction, suggestive of an important executive with more important matters on his mind.

When he was out of earshot one of his chaps said, "Cheeky cunt, Looks like Dali with that 'tash don't he?"

Later that day he came to my room to ask if I had got my boots. "You see, Kris, I would have served you myself but I am trying to impress a sense of social hierarchy into my chaps. I want them to understand that as top man in the department they should leave me free to handle the Public Relations and do the manual work themselves." He gave his moustache a magnificent twirl and ambled away.

The Sheikh and Barry became instant friends. Superficially improbable as the union seemed to be between the well spoken, sometimes very caustic Pakistani, and the wild, tearaway, semi-literate Australian, at a deeper level, under several layers of external expression, the seed from which they were sprung was the same. They recognised in each other, and held in high regard that propensity to hazard everything they possessed, both spiritual and material, on an impulse fuelled by caprice or pique.

When The Sheikh first came to Tiger Bay and told us of the fortune he had lost gambling, his story was received with scepticism.

The inhabitants of long term prisons by force of experience become very doubtful about stories of great wealth outside, as it is usually the precursor that establishes the necessary good will to ask for a loan of 50p.

So it was that the Sheikh was accepted at face value as a cannabis smuggler; his other claim of an eminent family background, and their riches, was put on file, so to speak, until some proof was offered.

The Sheikh was made aware of this scepticism; it drove him one day, to pull out from under his bed a canvas bag. It held the depositions of his trial, and photostat copies of all his bank accounts. It was all there in neat tabulated columns; the two year history of The Sheikh's compulsive neurosis, reduced to impersonal figures, brought to excruciating life by his anecdotal explanations of the various sums of money; withdrawals of twenty thousand pounds one week, and ten 'the next, with hardly anything going in. We pored over these accounts as philatelists might do over a batch of rare stamps.

At the end of our study Barry looked up and his eyes were bright with admiration. "It's true! You ugly black bastard, you really did blow all that money."

The Sheikh made a sideways movement of his head; a gesture of ethnic origin that signifies assent, but conveys the opposite meaning to Westerners.

"Every last goddamn penny," he said. There was a note of contentment in his voice. "And what is more I bounced a few cheques as well," he added.

"So what have you got out there now?" someone asked.

"I haven't as you chaps say, a pot to piss in when I go out, The Sheikh replied. "But," (he held up a hand dramatically to hold our attention) "don't write me off. I am not Sheikh Humayune Badur for nothing. When I am released from here, I intend to organise a caper that will net me one hundred million dollars US in four years, and then," (he wrung his hands and flicked his fingers as though they were covered in dust) "retire."

We didn't ask him how he was going to do this. Such a question may have revealed too many holes in his plan. In Tiger Bay, reminded of our own failures, and yet keeping alive the tireless flame of hope that somehow our battered fortunes would mend, we were inclined to leave a fellow prisoner his dreams; to let his imagination soar away clean out of the prison; to breathe the vapour trails left behind by his high-powered flight, and in that breathing to be recharged. It gave us a thrill of expectation just to hear The Sheikh say, "One hundred million dollars US," as though just hearing him say it, brought us nearer to it.

There was another area of the Sheikh's life which transported us beyond the complex walls; gave us a differently angled insight of recent history we had read about in the newspapers, but now related through personal visions.

It was triggered by a set of large, glossy, black and white photographs he kept in a shoe box. Moments frozen in celluloid, of friends and family groups taken at political functions or social galas. Tableaux of wealth and privilege; the flashlight catching the expensive glint on a wrist or ear. Men in their expensive, smart, buttoned up shervanis, the women bejewelled, and brilliant. There was no tension in those smooth, satisfied, party faces.

More often than not the focal point was a chubby balding man with the smiling assurance of a leader, the others arranged around him in patterns of importance and relative prestige. Here and there a white face, uninvolved but interested, broke the descending order of hierarchy that emanated from the power base in the centre.

The Sheikh prodded the photographs in an explanatory monologue; "Here is Mr Bhutto with the Defence Minister and his nephew. He was one of my school chums you know? Behind him talking to the Foreign Secretary that's Mark Tully, BBC correspondent out there. Speaks absolutely fluent Hindustani, you know?"

As The Sheikh moved his finger methodically across the photographs, I became engrossed in a private game, and began to study the faces intently. I was trying to discover in any of those carefree, camera-composed faces, the unguarded revealing expression that declared portents of terror for what was to come; some trace of precognition, or objective knowledge that the plump man so much the sought after, listened to, adulated centre of their world, would in the space of a very short time be taken at sunrise from an anonymous cell and be hung by the neck until dead; that not all the pomp, and ceremony, and power, he commanded as the first man in the land, nor all the machinations and pleadings of his illustrious colleagues in those photographs would save him from that jolting, dangling, end.

I mentioned this line of thought to The Sheikh who smiled indulgently.

"I have done something like that myself," he said. He thumbed through the stack of photographs and picked out one. "Then this one should interest you most," he said and handed it to me.

The photograph was like all the others, a dewy, black and white, ten by eight print. It had Mr Bhutto in the middle and some of the faces I had seen in the other photographs. The Sheikh and his uncle were also in this one, standing with their heads tilted reverentially towards Mr Bhutto, as if he had just made an important pronouncement.

I studied the photograph for several minutes as one would a picture puzzle, to see what the Sheikh was getting at. I found nothing appreciably different. The Sheikh was watching my face expectantly. Seeing no sign of recognition from me he jabbed at the corner of the photograph, "There! There. Look there," he said excitedly.

Two figures emerged in the corner, discreetly away from the camera's attention. One of them wore the turbanned headdress of a waiter in the colonial style. The other one whom he partially obscured in the act of passing by, stood in deeper shadow, legs apart. He was a smaller man and that was misleading, as I had imagined

67

him to be taller and broader, but something in the uncompromising squareness of his stance should have given me the clue to his identity. Also, he was not wearing the military cap with which I associated his face, although on a close scrutiny a discolouration on his chest could be discerned as campaign ribbons. It was the merest smudge of a man's image.

"Know who it is?" The Sheikh asked. Then not waiting for me to answer: "Don' t you think that is a unique photograph? The hangman and his victim. There are other pictures of them both together attending public functions, but this one is very subtle, don't you think. look at the way he is hidden in the shadows, waiting to pounce."

"Zia?" I asked for confirmation.

"Zia al Haq," he said. "The bastard who is running the country right now."

The Sheikh's image of the killer biding his time in the shades of obscurity, rolled around my head, and the scene in the photograph took on a deeper significance.

"My uncle and I were both present the day Mr Bhutto signed his own death warrant, you know," he said softly.

He started to speak about that decisive period of his life, and as he spoke, his face and eyes lit up and reflected the emotional drama of that time. I was carried along the compelling stream of his memories.

"It was in the first few days after Zia had declared martial law. At that time there was no, or there seemed to be, no personal bad feelings between the two.

"A group of us, a delegation I suppose you could call it, made up of the PPP (Peoples Progressive Party) headed by Mr Bhutto had gone to see General Zia. My uncle and myself were seated with a few others in an outer office, when Mr Bhutto and Zia came to the door of his office. It was quite clear from their faces that the meeting had not gone well, and hot words had been exchanged. I remember the incident so well. It is still vivid in my mind."

The Sheikh twirled his moustache reflectively. "Zia was standing over there by the door." The Sheikh pointed to the conveniently placed cell door, "and Mr Bhutto was here," he tapped the bars on his window. "The rest of us had got up and were getting ready to leave. He joined us and we were making our way out, then suddenly Mr Bhutto turned round and said to Zia 'Do you realise that what you have done is punishable by death?' He didn't just say the words, he shouted them as though he was addressing a servant. We were all completely stunned by what he had said, and the way he had said it. I don't think he even fully realised the implications. But he was like that, very impulsive. He never reasoned out anything, just spoke with his heart. Anyway we left that place in one piece that day, but there was never any doubt in any of our minds that from that day in Pakistan, there was one grave and two men to fill it. It was one, or the other."

I sat riveted by his story; to hear the account from someone so close to that incident was like looking at history through a microscope. It vaguely comforted me to know that even at the apex of national power structures, events were shaped, and changed, by irrational comments or personal threats, and abuse.

It was not difficult to imagine the scene. There was Bhutto, the portly irascible exponent of rhetoric, so recently deposed from his seat of power, and there facing him the military man who had emerged from the sidelines, mastered the moment, and captured the prize, while the politician was watching his other opponents.

It was also easy to imagine the frustrated, empty-handed politician stomping out of that room. Selected aides in the outer waiting room look up anxiously. Their leader's face gives them no cause for jubilation. Does he see in those dependant faces the first tentative signs of disappointment or doubt; is there by look or gesture an indication of a realignment of allegiances?

He feels the overwhelming need to reassert himself. His politician's mind knows the power of the slogan and the catchphrase. He knows how a defiant exclamation can become the cornerstone of a crusade.

In the act of going out with his flock, a seed lying hidden in the debris of his thoughts comes to life; it demands recognition, and before he can guess at what manner of grotesque tree it may grow into, the words escape his lips in a rush of adrenalin.

"Do you realise that what you have done is punishable by death?"

I envisaged these scenes, as The Sheikh described the incident, and I understood his summary of it, "That from that day in Pakistan there was one grave and two men to fill it."

After that talk with The Sheikh, so far removed from the usual prison chatter, I became a regular visitor to his room to listen to his reminiscences.

To everyone's astonishment The Sheikh and Barry became inseparable.

From the first day they started to insult each other racially, and personally; with them it seemed to be a private game, a bizarre method of communication. Their camaraderie appeared to stem from it. They were like quarrelsome brothers, verbally sparring and feinting, but in the end prepared to unite in some common cause. When a couple of prisoners were moved to the Lazy L with whom Barry had a long-standing feud, and he feared he would be ambushed, it was The Sheikh who walked with him, a six inch blade tucked up his sleeve until the trouble blew over.

Despite vague assertions that he was going to get in touch with, 'those chaps from GA' (Gamblers Anonymous) a rehabilitative course that the Lazy L allowed some inmates to take part in, The Sheikh still had not wholly committed himself, and continued to gamble on the horses.

He joined forces with Barry and they made their bets jointly with one of the bookies on another wing.

Their gambling partnership moved into a higher gear when they decided to open up as bookmakers themselves. There was a sudden gap in the profession when one of the practicioners had to retire in a hurry and be transferred out of the Lazy L to another prison, when he was unable to pay out all the winners after a Saturday afternoon's racing.

Barry and The Sheikh very nearly suffered the same fate on their inaugural day of business; The Sheikh's expensive gold watch had to be pawned to save the day. The following week they won back everything they had lost, and The Sheikh got his watch back. From that shaky start they grew in stature, and until the day Barry was 'shanghaid' to an unknown destination they prospered.

During this time of easy-come finances, weekend hooch drinking and ganja smoking parties became an event in the social calendar of Tiger Bay.

Barry's room used to be kept, as befits someone who does not know from day to day when he is going to be taken down the punishment block, in a state of minimum maintenance order; bare of large personal belongings that could not be bundled together hastily. It used to exude a makeshift, camp atmosphere. But after he had become rich through his activities as a bookmaker all that changed. Hitherto sneered at fixtures like curtains, and record players, with elaborate speakers were installed, and under his bed there was that symbol of affluence, the cardboard box filled with tea and sugar and tinned fruit.

They were generous with their profits, and I was frequently invited to an 'at home' in their rooms. On these occasions a gallon of hooch personally brewed by Barry and known to us as chateau Billabong, would be brought out of some devious hiding place. Dope pipes constructed from empty plastic bottles, and the stems of ballpoint pens; were also much in evidence.

On these occasions my pleasure at being invited was marred by a tinge of envy; for as their fortunes ascended, mine seemed to be balanced on the other end of the seesaw and was descending rapidly.

It was as though a malign star had singled me out for attention, poised above my head, ever ready to obstruct my path with sequences of unforeseen and painful events.

The first and most bewildering of these was not so much a single event as a gradual emergence of a state of affairs, where all the signs pointed to an eventual outcome which I refused to accept. My wife Daisy had stopped writing to me.

Chapter 8

Letters which had arrived with heartwarming regularity week after week through the long fourteen month period of my days on remand, and continued to arrive through the first two years of my life as a convicted prisoner at the Lazy L, had strengthened my belief that no matter what else went wrong for me, Daisy would always be there as loyal and steadfast as ever.

Her letters were always so full of hope for our futures, and encouragement for the present. I felt humbled by her courage and fortitude. That tenuous contact, by way of her letters was my only link with my home and family; my anchor in the past. If I could hold on to that lifeline all would be well in the end, I told myself. In one of her early letters she had, at the end, in what I imagined was the product of her misery and loneliness, drawn a little flower on a little stem. She was sending it she said with her love, to cheer me up.

The next letter had the same little flower—and the next, and the next. Born of her tears and frustration at wanting to help me, but unable to do so in more practical terms, the little flower became a symbol of continuity; an evocation of happier times. It transcribed her feelings about hopes for the future into the parallel lines of the stem and the curves of the petals. I was sustained by its message. It became a ritual habit for me to look at the end of the letter first, to see if the flower was there before I read the contents. And if the news was depressing; spoke of hardship and financial troubles, of unexpected bills to meet or any of the variety of problems I had left her to face alone, the little flower at the end seemed to lessen the impact; seemed to say in its wordless way that in spite of the setbacks she would survive them, and that the family and my home were intact and waiting for me. If her letters had contained no more than that single drawing, it would have sufficed; words would have been a needless embellishment. The flower would have said it all.

I had become accustomed to the vacuum world I lived in. No rent, no rates, no bills of any sort to worry about; no threatening solicitors' letters, no business worries, no hiding behind lampposts at sight of any vehicle that remotely resembled my bank manager's. The stresses that burden the life of a practising member of a business society, had been exiled by order of the Home Office from my mind; so that when Daisy spoke of them I could not feel the reality of the emergency. I reacted to her news in the way that news of an earth tremor in San Fransisco may have affected my mind; sympathetically, but in practical terms unhelpfully.

It was perhaps in reply to one such letter describing a household crisis, like the terminal collapse of the old washing machine; and a tired plea of "I don't know where the money is going to come from this time" where I could imagine her voice speaking the words she had written, that I had written back commiserating with her about the washing machine, or whatever it was, and in the next paragraph asking her if she could send me a pair of sandals.

A month went by. The next letter, told of further emergencies with the reconditioned washing machine she had just bought and exclamations of horror at the price of children's clothes. There was no mention of my sandals, but the flower was still there at the end of her letter. I wrote back, tut tutting about her bad luck with household appliances, and reminded her about my sandals.

Another month elapsed, and she wrote to me again. The pattern of her woes had not altered: there was no mention of my sandals. Thinking back about that time and the way our relationship changed, my memory is aided by some grubby tea-stained diary notes that have survived: with them, and illuminating flashes of retrospection, and dips into her letters, which I have kept, I am able to reconstruct the chronology.

A growing irritation about my sandals, aggravated by an infection of athlete's foot, found expression in a letter. I could not understand how someone who had once been so solicitous for my welfare; writing urgent letters to the Home Office, and the prison Governor, demanding every statutory right I had as a prisoner awaiting trial was observed, could now, fail to fulfil so slight a request. The reply I had from her had a distant coldness that was like a slap in the face. One line of that pivotal letter remains in my memory like a splinter in tender flesh. It read: "We make our beds, and we have to learn to lie in them".

There was no little flower at the end of it. The empty space screamed a message. I read the letter several times and like a small stone set loose to run down a ravine it unloosened other words she had spoken; unearthed from the incline other images. I remembered one of the very few kindly officers at Winchester coming to me the day after I had been sentenced: he told me that he had seen my wife on television the night before being interviewed for Southern-Television.

"Has anyone told you what she said, Krishnamma?" he asked.

I shook my head mutely.

"It was only on for a few minutes, but she came over really well," he continued. "She said, if it takes a hundred years the children and I will be waiting for him when he gets out."

The man looked at me for a reaction. I conjured up a smile from some instinctive part of my personality, like a boxer who smiles when he is confused or hurt.

"Is that what she really said?" I asked.

"Straight up," the man replied. His face became serious, softer.

"I wouldn't joke about family and that. That's exactly what she said."

A mixture of emotions coursed through me then, in that sterile observation cell they had put me in; to better study, they said, the effect the ten year sentence passed on me the day before was having.

I felt pride at being associated with a human being who could utter such a foolishly impractical and heroic statement: knew that her intention was that somehow I would hear of it; that the words were intended solely for me; to put some heart into me when heart was at a premium. I felt self pity too, and despair and frustration, and I don't know what else: but this I do know, that as the officer related bits that he could remember from the television programme, the tennis ball that was lodged in my throat became impossible to hide, and I looked away.

That was my Daisy—she would wait a hundred years for me.

Later, when the varied sentences passed on me and the fifteen other co-defendants had become a fact of our lives, and we had nerved ourselves to discuss earliest dates of release with parole, or the latest dates without it, we became aware in a gloomy, stoical sort of way of the prison phenomenon known as the 'Dear John': a euphemism for a letter that ended a marriage or a liaison. None of us had been to prison before; and each, consistent with his optimism or realism, evaluated the chances of their marriages surviving the lengths of their sentences. There were very few realists amongst us; imagining or persuading ourselves to believe that going to prison was like being posted overseas as a member of the armed forces or something similar.

From the earliest days, as the 'Dear Johns' began to arrive for some of the others, I experienced a feeling of immunity: it would never happen to me. The others who knew Daisy accepted that I was exempt; not without envy, for they all knew how purposefully I had strode down the paths of infidelity.

Even when the twelve volumes of depositions produced painstakingly by the prosecution, over a period of eight months' surveillance, proved beyond doubt, that I had been less than virtuous as a married man: illustrated with documentary evidence of hotel bookings and airline tickets, that I had dallied on more than one occasion with the pale flowers that bloom in the shaded environment of a casino operator's life—even then, despite the hurt and loss of face these revelations must have caused her, she did not forsake me.

Once, on a weekly appearance at the magistrate's court, a new disclosure of a weekend I had spent in Paris with company, came painfully to light. Her eyes were red and anguished with tears shed, and unshed, as she looked at me reproachfully.

"Oh, Suri," she whispered, "I would have loved to have gone with you to Paris just once, but you never took me."

With all my transgressions coming home to roost; in my abject misery and penitence I could have kissed her feet and asked for forgiveness. Instead I hung my head and looked down at my own feet and mumbled, "What can I say, or do now, lassie?"

Then, brave heart, compassionate human being, my Daisy hugged me and kissed me, and we felt the wetness of each other's tears. She straightened my tie and wiped the tears from my eyes to make me presentable for the court appearance.

I thought of those events in the past and could not reconcile the essence that was implicit in them, with the new indifferent Daisy who was emerging in her recent letters. It was as though the omission of the flower was the only way she knew how to say 'Dear John' to me.

Chapter 9

As I considered these selectively exhumed skeletons from the past I was gripped by a strange premonition.

The spore that created it was my avid reading of books and articles that dealt with the paranormal. I had lately been reading the writings of Carlos Casteneda; strange, fantastic stories purporting to be fact of an Indian sorcerer, and the neophyte who wanted to emulate him.

One section dealt with personal power symbols: the suggestion that with training and apprenticeship under a master in these arts, it is possible to recognize and obtain objects that act as 'protectors' in your life; that it is possible through certain rituals to imbue inanimate objects with powers to affect people's lives. However fanciful, and farfetched, I found this notion, and inconsequential to my study of the paranormal generally, I could not relieve myself of the nagging idea that when Daisy stopped drawing the little flower at the end of her letters, a power symbol that protected me had left my side. I could not pick that idea out of my head with the instrument of rationality.

So I just let it lie there in the corridors of my consciousness, like a protruding impediment on the floor; disregarding it most of the time, but forced to recognize its presence when I tripped over it. It is my recollection that during that time a chain of unpleasant incidents made me stumble on several occasions.

Daisy's flowerless letters became scarcer and scarcer, and finally after several of my letters over a three month period had remained unanswered, I decided to ask the welfare department at the Lazy L to help. They said they would call her and have some news for me in a few days.

A couple of days later I was summoned to the wing office by the PA system. "AG wants a word with you," the screw in the office said.

I knocked and went in. Peter Quinn was sitting behind his desk; a hunched left shoulder holding the telephone receiver in place against his ear, while he made notes on a pad on his knee. I was about to leave, but he motioned with his pen for me to sit down. He looked as rustic as ever, in a tweed jacket, leather patched at the elbows.

"How's things?" he asked, as he put the telephone down.

I made some suitable reply; relieved to know by the smile on his face that I was not in any sort of trouble.

"Nothing important—just a message from the welfare department to say they've been in touch with your wife, and she's going to write to you presently. How is Daisy by the way? No problem is there?"

I was about to say, no problem, and change the subject or leave the room but there was a hint in his voice which suggested a man who had half a story.

I recalled, as he referred to her by her first name, that when I had first arrived at the Lazy L three years previously, he had made two or three phone calls on my behalf, and in the ensuing conversation realised incidentally that they shared the same political affiliations. Daisy had also asked me to pass on her best wishes to him at Christmastime and other appropriate occasions. After that; like the Cambridge tie, it seemed to me, I was made welcome in his office for nothing more important than a social chat: I felt comfortable in his presence, discussing topics which were outside the normal range that existed between a prison official and a prisoner. Partly because of that consideration and partly because I had not discussed the problem with anyone, and the effort of containing it within myself was beginning to reflect in preoccupied moods, I outlined the deterioration in our relationship.

As I was speaking, I discerned in the way that he was listening, and nodding his head, and finishing sentences for me, that what I was telling him was not entirely new to him.

The thought occurred to me, that those unobtrusive, faceless men, who worked in the censor's office may have gleaned a lot from our letters. Had they, like watchful nurses, reported a change in the temperature of our relationship to the doctor responsible for my welfare? I felt uneasily like a patient whose condition is being kept secret from him.

"You see," he said when I had finished, "the welfare are in an invidious position in this kind of situation."

"What do you mean, Peter?" I asked.

"Well, when they are asked to mediate or intervene as you've just asked them to do, there have been other cases, where in the end the marriage has broken down, and they have been blamed as a contributory factor, which is why they referred this matter to me."

"What matter? You're talking as though there is some sort of crisis," I said, aware that my voice had become a little uneven. "All I've been told is that she will get in touch with me—that's the message you just gave me; which I suppose they could have given me themselves. In fact I don't know why they didn't. Is there something else I should know about?"

For what seemed an inordinately long time in the circumstances he did not answer; just kept pushing the yellow pad on his table with a forefinger into different positions.

As the silence grew it bred dreadful thoughts; awoke ghoulish phantoms from their slumber in my imagination: the children...one of the children...in an accident...fatally injured...and Daisy, cracked up under the strain...under sedation.

When he did speak, what he had to say came as a relief; just left me puzzled and vexed.

"Well, yes, there is," he said finally, carefully. "Apparently Daisy gave them a bit of stick about why they were bothering her and so on. That in itself doesn't matter—they're used to that. But they have also heard from your probation officer on the Isle of Wight to say that he can't get your home situation report completed for parole, because she refuses to see him. Apparently, he has rung her up a few times to try and fix a day when he can call round at the house to see her, but she won't agree to this—just says everything is the same as it was last year when he made his report, and sees no point in seeing him again. He's tried to explain to her that he is required to visit the home of prospective applicants for parole each year, and fresh reports have to be made out. But she's adamant; she doesn't want to see him. So he's got in touch with the welfare here, to see if they can cast any light on the matter; and as I say they've informed me."

"I don't know what to make of it," I said.

"I wasn't going to tell you all this," he continued, "since the message was that she was going to write to you. She'll probably explain it all in her letter. Anyway, I'm on holiday for two weeks. When I get back, if you still haven't heard I'll call her for you if you like. It's probably all a storm in a tea cup, with some simple explanation."

I agreed that that appeared to be the best course of action, and left.

The information I had been given added another dimension to the puzzle of her silence, but at least the horrors of my imagination had been put to sleep again: she was going to write soon. And when she did, the conundrum would be resolved. I would write back cheerfully, not mentioning my sandals; the little protective flower would reappear in her letters, and all would be well again. I went back to my room more optimistically than I had emerged from it.

Chapter 10

Lately, the state of my finances had been moving from one crisis to another. My lifestyle in the prison needed about five pounds a week to be sustained: my wages were one pound ten pence per week. I had managed to keep the books balanced by playing or running games of poker; by dealing in dope, and buying and selling any of the paintings, or artefacts some of the prisoners produced.

Then the hard times set in. The regular losers at the poker games with utter disregard for my welfare, selfishly quit the game, and started playing Kalooki in the card room; a game which does not have the cut and thrust, and concealed deviousness of poker, and ipso facto, at which, I was no good.

The dope situation was bleak; and I was currently involved in the retail end of the trade: that is to say, I sold someone else's dope, in one pound deals, at a commission rate of one for myself for every four I sold. It entailed a deal of chasing around the prison, getting the money together from individual customers on pay day, to pay the wholesaler—just like being a retailer outside, with all the attendant risks of sudden departures to unreachable destinations, or an honest and simple aversion to parting with money. The hard luck stories I had to listen to, aged me considerably. I discovered I had an unerring knack of unearthing and enrolling as customers, all the chiselers and conmen at the Lazy L. They were eager enthusiastic buyers on credit; dismissing the amount they had to fork out on pay day, as small potatoes, but when that day of reckoning arrived, it was like trying to wrest a bag of bananas from King Kong.

Add to that, my own fastidious propensity for sampling the goods (how else was I, as a conscientious tradesman, to ascertain that my customers were getting a square deal?) and the net result was that I was not making any headway against the financial tide. I owed a total of about twenty pounds to my creditors; not a sum of money which would have unsettled me a few months previously, but which then, with all my tunnels of revenue blocked, did not allow me to fall asleep at night as virtuously as I used to. A decent windfall would wipe my worries away overnight, but for the life of me I could not foresee where it was going to come from.

It was in this becalmed state, that I had, in a spirit of desperation decided to crash into the 'make it and sell it market'. I studied the articles being made at the Lazy L, and it seemed to me that soft toys made with fabric and foam rubber, offered the best hope for someone so singularly untalented at making anything as myself; but when I thought of the nuts and bolts of the enterprise, the patterns and diagrams, the cutting and shaping, not to mention the sewing and stuffing of these products, my initial zeal at the prospect diminished.

What I needed I realised in a moment of self congratulatory illumination, was a work's manager; a stout fellow, preferably a bit stupid, who would do all the work for a pittance say a handful of rice, and a chappatti, while I raked in the profits. I advertised for such a stout stupid fellow on the wing, and in the prison, by word of mouth, and waited for applicants to line up outside my door; practising an encouraging pep talk for the one I would choose, and a patronizing dismissive one for those I would reject. After a week had gone by without a single enquiry for the post; and just as I was about to abandon the project, coincidence resolved the dilemma.

Joe Fellatio came knocking on the doors of Tiger Bay one weekend with a clutch of items for sale or barter. He had a reputation in the prison as a purveyor of defective goods; their primary and only selling point being their extreme cheapness. Usually, when he was trading he looked like a walking junk shop. That day he had on his person, or hanging from it, a battered radio, a set of headphones, a guitar whose warped condition and lack of strings suggested the musicality of a shovel, a pair of training shoes tied together by their laces, and slung over his shoulder, a couple of framed Frank Frazzetta prints, and under one arm, a bundle of grimy fur fabric which vaguely resembled an animal from the rodent or reptile family.

He started to describe his wares in terms that would have qualified him for execution under the provisions of the Trade Descriptions Act on several counts, while I was held fascinated by the bundle under his arm. What manner of creature could it be? Weasel? Skunk? Armadillo? And what was that erect penis shaped appendage growing out of its forehead? Here surely was a clue to its genealogy. I mentally listed the numerous animals of whose existence I was aware, that exhibited their genitalia on their foreheads.

While I was conjecturing thus, he prattled on about the pristine quality of his goods.

"Only been worn twice; no, tell a lie, three times," he said, smacking the training shoes together, and deftly covering up a bald patch on the heel of one of them; anxiously peering into my face to see if I had noticed.

"What's that under your arm, wanker?" I asked casually.

A look of honest admiration, of unrestrained candour, flooded his wrinkled simian countenance; and he showed the assorted sizes and configuration of his ochre teeth, in a wide engaging smile.

"Bloody marvellous!" he said. "That's bloody marvellous. Here I am rabbiting on about this other load of garbage, and you knew all the time the one thing of real value I had on me. Spotted it right off didn'tcha? That's what you call business acumen 'ennit? It explains why you buggers 'ave got all our shops now. That's why you Indians are so good in commerce. Real connosewers. What chance did I have, silly Englishman? H'y'are. Fairdo's. Fair's fair, you've had me over. It's yours for 50p." And he thrust the bundle of fur at me.

I shook hands with the animal cautiously, and examined it at arm's length.

"What is it?" I asked eventually.

"Ha Ha, Ho Ho, I like that. Nice sense of humour, so early in the morning. You should be on the wireless with jokes like that son. How many animals do you know that have a trunk?"

"Oh trunk, yes I see what you mean; now that you mention it. I thought..."

"Never mind what you thought. You obviously don't know your genus pachyderm as well as me. Look at the workmanship! And these, look at these," he said, jabbing and nearly dislodging two caterpillar-shaped strips of black material that had been stitched on, in approximately the correct position.

"Yes, yes. I see them," I said excitely, for now that I knew the beast to be an elephant, I was getting into the spirit of spotting recognizable features.

"Eyebrows," he announced loftily. "I am the only one in this nick that puts eyebrows on." He expanded at length that it was small sensitive touches like that, that made his creations so sought-after by the criminal classes. From somewhere within the disorganized chambers of recent memory, a descriptive word was trying to sneak out.

"It's tera or tetra something," I blurted out.

He stopped in mid sentence, and looked at me with a mixture of puzzlement and concern.

"What are you burbling on about. I told you not to take them hormone pills in the morning, didn't I?"

I ignored his badinage, for this was a rare and fruitful moment, when a normally useless pastime had paid off. I had, during the course of the past year, filled an exercise book with unusual bits of information under different headings. I found the book and turned to the page triumphantly. Under a list of esoteric sciences I found what I wanted, and pointed it out to him.

"Now stand over there, and in a loud clear voice, read out what it says on that line," I commanded.

He took the book from me suspiciously and in his rasping, gravelly voice, began to read.

"Teratology; the study of malformations or freaks in nature."

"So? Thanks for showing me this. It's the kind of information I've always wanted to have under me belt. Very handy that. We must have a long discussion about your personal problems some other time when I'm less busy. Now, can we get back to the sale of this merchandise? You can give me 50p cash, or 20p now, and the other 40p in two weekly payments of 20p each."

"I wouldn't give you 5p for it, mush," I said. "Besides I want to establish for my own peace of mind that beneath that insolent and disreputable exterior, you are an honourable man of science—a teratologist in fact, and this…this, well, this thing is a visible model of an animal you hope to discover. Have I got all that right?"

"Are you suggesting my elephant is a freak?" he asked trying to look indignant, or at least, insofar as physiognomy would allow a portrayal of that emotion; his features being cast in a perpetual grin or leer. "What's wrong with it? It's got all the bits and bobs an elephant should have 'ennit? A trunk, eyebrows, four legs. What more do you want for 50p? Blood?"

"Well, how can I put this, Joe," I ventured gently. "It's a matter of some delicacy, and…please treat this as the merest amateur's suggestion, but don't you think your animal might have faced the world with more confidence if it had *two* ears."

"That's another characteristic I've noticed about your race—very observant people," he replied unabashed. Paranoid about symmetry. Fancy noticing a trifling discrepancy like that. What makes you people so mathematically inclined? Always counting."

"It comes from a long apprenticeship of peering at small beads and trinkets when we are trading with foreign spivs," I replied.

"I was warned about you Krishnamma, even before I come here this morning. They said, don't go down that spur, that Indian maharishi will have you over with his googlies, and long words. What chance has an honest tradesman got against the likes of you? Anyway, clever bollocks, I know it's only got one ear; I am well aware of that fact, but if you'll just sign this piece of paper sayin' it's a sale, I'll have it stitched on before you can say chicken vindaloo."

With that he produced from a recess of his overalls a triangular piece of cloth in which, to all appearances, he had blown his nose several times. I was instantly converted to the desirability of a one eared elephant.

"I don't know, matey, 7p is a lot of money to hand out; over one fifteenth of one's earnings."

"I see. I get the picture. First it was 5p, now it's gone up to 7p. What you're after is a haggle. Fancy yourself as a haggler, do you?"

I was aware of where the devious little bastard was leading the conversation and to what end; but by a massive compromise of my ideals, and by a baffling and optimistic pattern of reasoning, I had tentatively formed the notion that here, before my very nose was the stout stupid work's manager I sought; so I let myself be led.

"Right," he said, joyously, clapping his hands together, and dumping his impedimenta on the bed. "You know the rules: where are the makings?"

In Joe's book of haggling rules, the primary, and possibly the only one, was that copious quantities of tea had to be drunk before opening bids could be tendered. I had fallen foul of rule one, several times before, and since he never had any tea of his own, it was always my stock that was depleted disastrously at these haggling contests. I pointed to the cupboard and he trundled off with a jug to get the water.

While I was waiting, I cleared a space on a high shelf on which I stored bits and pieces I did not have an immediate use for, and placed the elephant on it. It immediately adopted an acrobatic pose, and I noted with no surprise, that one of its hind legs was stuck out at an angle, like a dog having a pee, so that its balance was secured by three legs. What with its black button eyes, earnestly crossed, its single ear, three functional legs, fly away eyebrows, and priapus trunk, it was the sorriest and most uncuddly soft toy imaginable. It evoked the protective response of an orphaned child.

As I stood there sympathising with its misfortune in having a designer as erratic as Joe Fellatio, I was not to know that long after that day had passed; long after Joe had finished his sentence; I would perform compassionate plastic surgery on him; uncross his eyes, deflate his trunk, find a mate for his ear, and make him a cap from the sleeve of an old green prison cardigan; and that when I finally left the electronic embrace of the Lazy L, Ele, as I came to christen him, would be one of the few possessions I would take out with me; and that in the years to come in the big world outside, he would have a special niche, always on a high place, to watch over me, anywhere I made my home; that there would come a time when I would not have parted with him for a thousand pounds. The one characteristic I did not tamper with was his crooked leg; his three-legged trick, inviting applause gave him an air of theatrical panache that was irresistible.

When Joe came back with the tea, as I had anticipated, we did not haggle. He had managed to scrounge his mid morning mug of tea, and mission accomplished, he sat down contentedly in the doorway with his back against the jamb, and proceeded to unpick a couple of dog ends, to make himself a rollup. It emerged as we gossiped that he was also having a lean time financially, and owed the bookmaking firm of Barry and The Sheikh a total of four pounds. That was a lot for Joe.

"It's nothin' really. It's just in 'ere it seems a lot. I got a limit with them of five quid," he said uneasily. I told him of my own impecunious state, and he seemed a little relieved to hear that my problem was five times the size of his.

"It's all relative, 'ennit?" he said cheerfully. "I owe four nicker and think that's a lot. You owe twenty, and think that's a lot. Did you hear how much McLoy lost on E wing. Know who I mean? The bookie."

"I heard a vague story in the gym," I said.

"Hundred and fifty quid in the bath house. It come on top accidentally. Screws were lookin' for a blade that went missing from the kitchen. Took the place apart lookin' for it, and come across the pound notes. Joke of it was, the knife never left the kitchen. They found it in the trough they peel the spuds in. Bet he's sick, eh! Can't bear to think of losin' a hundred and fifty nicker outside, let alone in 'ere. Can you?"

While the conversation was about money; ways to acquire it, ways to spend it, or hide it, I used the words, "Stout, stupid fellow," a few times in a ruminative sort of style, like an absentminded soliloquy, to see if the words would float around the room, and settle on the scrawny shoulders of the imp in the doorway. Each time I thought they were about to land; thus allowing me to reveal my blueprint for financial salvation, I was dissuaded by what I had heard and knew personally, about this layabout, who had once defined work to me, as getting out of bed in the morning. Somehow, I felt the description, stout stupid fellow, had to be interpreted imaginatively to fit him.

Further, would a person who answered readily to the sobriquet of Fellatio, inspire confidence in the products of a company of which he was work's manager? It was one of those executive decisions I felt I could not take without more data; so I let the words out again.

"What's goin' on 'ere. What you keep repeating 'stout stupid fellow' to yourself like that. I hope you're not talkin' about me, mate. I'll have you up before the Race Relations' Board," he said, grinning at me and winking.

I didn't answer; just gave him a calculating business tycoon's look.

"Is this one of those joke things, like knock knock, who's there and so on. You say stupid fellow and I say what stupid fellow. and then you come in with the punch line: that sort of childish pastime.

Through the open doorway I heard the creaky rumble of the food trolleys being brought in for lunch, and the clatter of the serving utensils being set out. It was time to play my ace in the hole.

"How would you like to make a lot of money, Mr Fellatio?" I breathed.

In an instant, he was prostrate on the floor, clasping my legs in a desperate embrace.

"Master, speak, master. O wise and holy guru from the East. I await your bidding," he cried.

The words I was trying to fit on to him, were poised motionless over his head. It was as he was passionately kissing my instep, that I knew I had my stout stupid work's manager. Now, there was nothing to stop me from going into full production. Already my brain was working on the fine tuning of this operation—whether to offer my workforce twenty, twenty five, or thirty per cent of the profits.

Brusquely, I brushed the cringing creature and his dandruff off my shoes, and announced a board meeting for that evening at six thirty.

"O goody," he chirupped. "Board meetings usually have cups of rosy and a little something to smoke. Is that not so, master?"

"We'll discuss the catering arrangements when you get here," I paused, as high powered businessmen sometimes do. "I run a tight ship here, Fellatio, I hope you understand that."

"Yes, master, I do," he assented.

I sensed he would have tugged his forelock too, but they were hanging down his back in long greasy strands. He picked up his belongings from the bed and looking up at Ele in the manner of a designer leaving behind his chef d'oevre he announced that it was a gift—a gesture he hoped would be the icing on the cake of our relationship.

I was tucked up in bed that afternoon, feeling pleased with the developments of the morning, even before the electronic clicks on the doors, sealed them for the hour long lock up between 5 and 6 o'clock.

Sleep-inducing imagination saw endless regiments of huggable teddy bears with the most inspiriting price tags around their necks.

Just before I fell asleep I had a peek at Ele. The chink between the curtains had made his kingdom on the shelf a place of light and shadow, and he presided over his territory while performing his mono drama on three legs; and it seemed that he winked at me as though he approved of my machinations.

Chapter 11

When I woke to the electronic release click on the door; a small sound, yet so powerfully compelling to one whose life is governed by its application; I spent a few complacent moments marshalling my thoughts on how best to convince my employee that the only reason for the formation of this company was (a) to get me out of debt (b) to make me rich enough to indulge in the pleasures I had become accustomed to.

Already I was beginning to doubt the wisdom of giving him the title of Works Manager. It sounded too elevated and inviolable a position. It could so easily go to his head and balloon it out of control. Why not just call him Worker one, containing as it did the implicit threat that if he got out of line he would be replaced by Worker two and Worker three. I would have to make it clear from the outset that I would not tolerate any modernistic guff about workers' rights and the plethora of unprofitable concessions that slogan spawns. No; what I would have to do was to collect a few age-old falsehoods like, 'A good day's work is its own reward' and other incredible and disused mottoes like the Nobility of Labour, and disguise them, as is the practice of the day, in business language—worker incentive schemes, bonus points and so on, and thereby achieve the same end. For sure, I would discharge my side of the contract by occasionally throwing a couple of tea bags into his shovel as he worked; but a share in the profits? That didn't seem such a good idea. Above all, I had to cultivate his mind to accept the notion that the degree of his happiness was linked proportionately to my accumulation of wealth. If only I had the resources of a Brave New World, I would have him crooning as he sewed: I am Worker one, I love my work. The harder I work the richer my master gets. That makes me so happy. I am glad I am Worker one.

It will be appreciated that warmed and relaxed by these honourable capitalistic thoughts I was totally unprepared for what happened next.

He was a few minutes late and I expected him to slink into view frothing apologies; with downcast eyes and sorry expression. When he did appear he bounded towards me like a rubber ball down a garden path. There was no sign of penitence in his gait or demeanour.

As he came closer I perceived that he was not bouncing so much as dancing.

I registered with considerable trepidation that he had shaved *and* bathed. It was generally accepted on the wing, that he bathed or shaved on special occasions such as the summer solstice or Christmas: for him to have done both on the same day signified some momentous event. I decided to handle the interview rather carefully; and swallowed the cold words of reproach I was about to deliver about his lateness.

"Where's the tea then?" he snarled. "I haven't got all evening to waste over a half-baked idea to make money. If you want me to listen to your rubbish, get crackin' and make a strong cuppa. And don't undercut the milk and sugar either." I was about to administer a karate chop to his knees to bring him to his senses; and back into place in my fantasy, when he suddenly whipped out two enormous joints whose size made my eyes gasp.

"Of course," he continued, "if you don't want to make the tea, that's OK with me, and I'll go somewhere else with these for a cuppa. Get my meaning?

He then waved them under my nose.

I am not a foolhardy person. Even before he had completed his threat I was hurrying down the corridor with two tea bags in a jug, towards the boiler. If I was seen to be smiling bravely it belied the tears of envious rage I was holding back. The fates had conspired against me while I slept. This man whom I had selected with so much care; this layabout wino, whom I was going to shape and mould into a captain of industry and commerce no longer needed me. Deus ex machina. I would find out the details soon enough.

Heaving a prodigious sigh of resignation and stifling a sob, I hurried back to my cell. There, between sips of tea and tokes of joint, he told me with many a dramatic embroidery, how he had parlayed a deficit of four pounds into a credit of six. In other words as he explained to me a dozen times, he had won ten pounds on that Saturday afternoon's racing. Luck, he said, did not figure in the winning formula. It was all done with skill and judgement. In that, he was no different to every gambling man who ever recounted a winning coup. Sitting comfortably on my only chair, while I sat in his erstwhile position in the doorway; a visible manifestation of the reversal in our relationship; he grew expansive. The dope, which had recently entered the prison and was reputed to be very strong was living up to its reputation. After a few deep tokes we were both affected by it.

"Soft toys, eh!" he mused. "What do you know about it? Are you capable of hard graft? It's not all glamour and money y'know. You've never had stitcher's cramp or stuffer's elbow, have you?"

I shook my head thankfully.

The rest of his lecture couched in rhetoric amounted to this: I was living under the misapprehension shared by everyone outside the vocation, that soft toy manufacturing was a picnic. It seems I had not understood the minutely precise art it was; besides which, neurosurgery was a frenzied hack-about. A micro millimetre lost here or there on the cutting table, and the creation was a reject.

How he could say such things while evidence of his handiwork glared down in mute denunciation from the shelf was beyond me; but he did.

After he had preached to me thus for over half an hour, I decided it was time to express my own views and say something decisive at the meeting.

"How about smoking the other joint now?" I ventured.

He seconded the proposal, and made some more tea. It was during the smoking of this second joint that I somehow seemed to lose my grip on the purpose of the meeting and just sat there in a stoned haze of benevolence, while he prattled on.

It was one of those highs, when everything being said sounded terribly interesting, but I could not remember from second to second what had been said. I vaguely understood that he was trying to instil in me the right attitude towards our proposed undertaking. Quite clearly, he summarized, my motives were base, mercenary, even cavalier, for what was in truth a solemn and priestly function. I was advised to fill my mental vision with the happiness our products would bring to hundreds of little babas as they drooled over their teddy bears in bed. Only the finest, thoroughly examined models would ever leave our conveyor belt he intoned. Anything less would be an act of profanity directed against our cherubic clientele. There was to be no cheap Hong Kong, or backstreet Bombay workmanship he warned, as he nailed me with a meaningful eye. Our creations would reflect all that was best in British craftsmanship; clear and uncompromising.

"Fellatio Fine Arts, or Fellatio Fancy Goods. What do you think of that for starters," he asked, and with it brought me back from a long way away.

"Don't forget the babas," I said.

"What about the babas?"

"What do you suppose the mamas and dadas of the babas will do when they find out their babas favourite teddy was made by a firm with a name as…as, well, as open to misinterpretation."

He sprang up from the chair as though he had sat on something sharp; eyes ablaze with the thrill of discovery. "I've got it. I've got it," he squeaked, punching the air, and doing a more vigorous variation of the dance routine I had seen him perform earlier.

"By God this is good gear 'ennit? See how the ideas flow out of me, after I've had a puff. Not just a pretty face y'know."

Speaking in jerks, for the dance had drained his physical reserves, he elaborated his theme. It was not a name that had galvanized him to such animation. He was off on a completely different tack. We were to have another company; a subsidiary devoted to making adult soft toys.

"Adult?" I queried weakly. "You mean big giant teddy bears and pandas?"

He cast me a withering, pitying look. "Where have you been living all your life? In a monastery or what? Not big bloody giant anythings. Sex toys, you pillock. It's all the rage out there now. Vicars and bus drivers, they're all at it now, with them rubber dolls you pump up. Them with the special vibrating parts. See, this is where you are too slow for this game. You got to be able to spot a trend, and strike while the iron is hot."

"By all means," I said. "Let us strike while the iron is hot." It was the sort of stirring exhortation that I felt I could throw my weight behind.

"But to get things absolutely straight in my head—those toys are not for the babas are they?"

"Wassa' matter with you? How many times do I have to explain my ideas. I think I better draw you a few pictures hadn't I? Now, I'll go through it all one more time. *No;* these products are not for the babas. They got their own firm makin' kiddies toys. Got that? Now forget about the babas. These other toys I'm talkin' about is for their mamas and dadas and for their big sistas."

This last group of relatives must have forwarded an image from his memory or fantasy, for he leapt to his feet again:, this time to demonstrate by thrustful motions of his pelvis, and juggling movements around two imaginary grapefruit; that the sistas he had in mind were substantially endowed ladies indeed.

His imagination took off in several directions at once, as he sought to impress me with the viability of his ideas. We would shortly, he announced, be producing a group of soft toys under the licence of an evocative title: The Kama Sutra Classic Series, no less. Teddy bears, pandas, elephants and other suitable species drawn from the higher mammals, were to be depicted in foam rubber and fur, in various postures of sexual congress. Another opinion he held, and which he described as a sure fire winner, was a teddy bear constructed with a secret button on its left heel which when pressed would release a penis the size of a baseball bat from between its knees. I hardly had time to assimilate one idea before he was off on the next. They came out of the top of his stoned brain like sparks off a grinding wheel.

By the time his inventive fever had abated, I was totally confused about which of these products was to be our standard bearer.

"Well, what do you reckon? Got enough to be going on with ain't we? Brilliant 'ennit?" he asked, grinning. "Don't be shy. If you think it's brilliant, say so."

Dope sometimes has the effect of making me extremely cautious; but I was able to tell him with sincerity that as a visionary, the only competition he had was from Da Vinci and Wells.

He looked momentarily apprehensive. "We don't want any of them other geezers cuttin' in on my ideas," he declared. "If there's goin' to be any heavy stuff, you'll have to take care of it."

"Don't worry about a thing, kid," I growled. "I'll bury those two bastards if they try to mess with our copyright. I might even poke 'em in the eye with the Teddy with the big what'sit to soften 'em up first."

It was the least I could do for a partner who was trying to get some monetary mileage out of teddy bears stuck up each other.

"In the meantime, mum's the word," he urged. "We don't want any of this to get into the wrong hands. It's dynamite."

I checked under the bed, and down the corridor, and agreed that it was a matter of the highest sensitivity.

We shook hands fervently; swore each other to secrecy several times; and parted conspiratorially.

Chapter 12

The following week, no practical steps were taken to get into production; and I knew none would be, until he had spent or lost his winnings—but we did have two more top-level board meetings. I had become the chela to his guruship. By the time it came to discuss financial divisions my position was very weak. I needed the money and he, swaggering runt, did not; and worse, he knew it.

"Tell you what I'm gonna' do with you my man," he said, "seein' as how this is a one man show, like it's all down to me 'ennit? My brains, my sweat, my technology, it's all mine. All you have to do is get the raw materials, and even there, you won't have to get the foam rubber. I got my own source for that. The more I think about it, I don't REALLY need you, do I? Fairs fair, you're just a passenger, aintcha?"

I held up a hand for permission to speak.

"Yes, go on," he said, tapping his tiny feet impatiently.

"I wonder if your Worship could explain to a complete idiot such as I am what he means by technology. You see I had this notion that tech...."

"Technology. The means of production," he hissed. "Can't you understand simple English. My fuckin' scissors, my needle, and not any old needle, these are specially curved ones, my thread, my thimbles and other bits and bobs, mate. That's what you call technology."

I was struck speechless by his grasp of industrial shop floor matters, and tried a different approach.

I reminded him that it was I, his blood brother who had, not so many weeks ago, given him half a dozen highly inflammatory pornographic postcards depicting a loose-jointed threesome from Osaka, Japan; the ones which he had posted in strategic locations on his cell walls. I did not let him forget that I could have sold or traded them, but I had chosen to give them to him.

"That's what you call Brotherhood, Joe," I said piously. "A blood brother always reaches down to a fallen brother, to pull him up."

"Orright, Orright you're breakin' my heart. Tell you what I'm gonna' do with you. You get the stuff, except the foam rubber, an' I'll do the rest, and lemme see, we'll split down the middle—seventy-thirty. An' in case you're wonderin'; the seventy is for me."

Well, I whinged and whined so energetically, that I managed to raise my share to forty per cent; that was the best I could do.

With that issue settled I optimistically assumed we would get started; with that in mind I scrounged a piece of tatty pink fur fabric from an acquaintance, and carried it expectantly to Joe. I realised from his reluctance to start actual work, that he still had some portion of his winnings still intact.

"We don't want to rush into anythin' blindly like a bull in a china shop," he said vaguely. I'll have to get a pattern off what'isname on B wing first. Remember what Mao said to his troops when they wanted to go charging in?"

I told him I was not aware of this piece of anecdotal history. "Slowlee, slowlee, catchee monkee."

I was about to tell him that I had indeed heard of that proverb before, and had cause to remember it as a most insecure one; often while approaching monkee slowlee slowlee, he ups and runs away, and one ends up clutching thin air where monkee's tail should have been; I didn't, as I knew by previous experience that there was no agency on earth which could force him to do any extra work besides his daily stint at the laundry, until he had no more coins left in his pocket. So I carried my tatty pink fur fabric away with me, and waited. A classic example of the devious means by which the honest, fund-raising, capitalist entrepreneur, is held to ransom by the selfish, opinionated, technocrat.

A few days later he rushed into my cell in a state of nervous agitation, and flopped into my chair.

"Right, time I went to work," he said, manfully squaring his shoulders.

"Where's that bit of fur? I got an order for a teddy. Got to be ready to be handed out on a visit at the weekend." I made a simple deduction; he was broke. It was my turn to extract what bonus I could from the situation.

"I've been thinking of using it to cover my chair with," I said, "and besides, it troubles me greatly to go against Mao's advice. Remember? Slowlee, slowlee catchee, and all that. A great man like that, wouldn't have put it in his little red book unless he'd thought it out very carefully. He obviously had people like us in mind when he said it. I think we should think this whole operation through much more carefully."

"Never mind about Mao. You never want to take what them chinks say seriously. Strike while the iron is hot, that's what Montgomery used to say."

"Montgomery? Montgomery?" I queried. "I don't think I've heard of this gentleman. Was he one of Mao's lads on the long march?"

"Any bloody school kid knows who Montgomery of El Alamein was. Greatest bleedin' desert fighter that ever lived, that's who."

"You never want to take anything them Arabs say seriously," I said. "Sneaky lot of buggers, forever pinching each other's dates, and what they get up to with their camels doesn't bear thinking about. I think we should stick with Mao, don't you?"

Finally in desperation he shrieked, "You can have fifty per cent. Fifty-fifty right down the line, an' I'll do all the bleedin' work," he added petulantly.

I decided the company was ripe for a smooth takeover bid. I emptied him out of my chair, into the doorway where he belonged and sat down in the chairman's seat. It felt good to be driving at last. I outlined in clear unequivocal terms how the company was to be run, and our respective positions within it; I also laid down, giving him no room for improvisation, the designs our products were to take, and the response they were to elicit from our customers.

"The company is to fabricate teddy bears, plain and simple." I said. "Nothing fancy. You hear me. I want to see teddy bears the way they used to be when I was a baba. I do not wish to be associated with bears that have concealed wangs that spring out at people at the touch of a button. Never heard such rubbish! Do you realise, you lecherous little man, you could have whacked someone in the eye if that button had been pressed accidentally. Where would the company have been in a lawsuit then?"

He sat in the doorway glumly nodding his head.

"Lemme see now," I said, feeling a little sorry for him.

"I'll get the cloth, the thread and eyes. You get the foam rubber and do what little work there is to be done, and we'll split equitably as partners should, slightly off centre, seventy-thirty. And don't ask me who the seventy is for."

Well, he whinged and whined so adroitly, reminding me that he had not charged me for doing my laundry a couple of weeks previously, and introducing a preposterous claim to being my blood brother, and ending with a cretinous suggestion that brothers helped each other in times of shortage, (a sentiment he said I had expressed at some time in the past, and of which I had no recall,) that I relented in the end, and agreed to let him have forty per cent.

He carried my tatty pink fur away with him, and promised to convert it into a teddy bear in two days. As he was leaving I felt it incumbent on me to offer him some avuncular words of advice—some phrase, or saying that would put some backbone into him.

"Remember this," I said in my most dramatic voice. "The mightiest oak from an acorn grew."

"Mao or Montgomery?" he asked.

"Mary Poppins," I replied.

"Sounds about right for Mary Poppins," he said, ruefully as he trudged away.

A classic example of how the patient, canny entrepreneur gets the better of the independent, and insolent, technocrat sometimes.

Two days later, a few hours ahead of schedule there was a very chubby and cheerful teddy sitting on my bed for inspection.

I checked on the heel, behind the ears and other suitable places, there were no secret buttons, and nothing that would spring out at an unsuspecting person. The bear was neuter, buoyant, and altogether quite teddy bearish; I passed him fit for sale, at a price of three pounds.

We made the transaction on pay day and arranged ourselves in genuflection on either side of a hardback chair in the card room for the pleasantest part of the operation. Earlier, I had earnestly proposed that to make matters simpler and the figures round I should take two pounds and he could have what was left.

"Don't sound right to me," he said. "Is that a sixty-forty split?" he asked suspiciously.

I assured him that it was a device used by some of the most eminent men in accountancy, and was called rounding up; I failed to tell him that there were a couple of these gentlemen right there at the Lazy L, for practising variations of this technique in their business lives.

He wouldn't wear it, and demanded the partnership contract should be fulfilled to the letter. After a paranoid consultation of several textbooks, slide rules and charts he came up with the exact figure we should each receive.

So we shunted the coins back and forth across the seat of the chair until he had 120p and I had 180p in various columns of thicknesses. During this manoeuvre we watched each other's fingers at eye level for any deft sleight of hand movements. When the division was finally agreed to have been made, and the silver and copper coins stood facing each other like a greatly decimated army of chessmen, he extracted from my side 15p for the laundry he had done for me, and I took back from him 3p he owed me for a box of matches I had given him during the week. We were in business.

The durability of our partnership was always governed by his fortunes at horse racing; it was an unstated feature that I had accepted; so that as soon as he had a win I would stop taking orders or tout for more business.

In the early days of our life as soft toy manufacturers I made an interesting discovery about the provenance of that vital ingredient that gave our products their bounce: the foam rubber.

By evolving custom, in long term prisons, the chairs in the television room gradually progress from being impersonal functional objects, into symbols of personal territorial expression. After a man has sat in the same chair in the third row near the window for several months on end, for every minute that he is permitted to watch television, he starts to think of it as his chair, and refer to it as *my* chair. Once he has said that, he has staked a claim which could, on any night, be challenged; he has then to defend it, or vacate it. Either response could prove costly, for different reasons. It is therefore only the most ardent worshippers of the radiating screen who make these attachments.

Those of us who were occasional viewers in the interest of good health, usually enquired if the seat we were about to sit in belonged to anybody of muscular significance. If it did not, we sat down; if it did, we moved smartly on to the next one.

On our wing at that time there were three heavyweight wrestler-types whose sole pastime was watching television. Their combined IQ was 14; their combined weight unthinkable. They had developed extraordinary intellectual skills at regurgitating whole chunks of dialogue from programmes that suited them, like Coronation Street, and Cross Roads. They also held learned discussions, usually in the toilets, about what certain characters from the spiritual slums of Dallas might do in the next episode. When their predictions proved correct they beamed at each other neanderthally and said, "Told ya, didn' I".

One night, the biggest of these, after grunting and farting on his chair for a few minutes (customary preliminaries before watching a programme he particularly enjoyed) slowly, mountainously, stood up and surveyed his chair.

"Ooos bin at me fookin chair? It feels all loompy like," he said.

As if on cue, the second biggest one lumbered to his feet.

"And oos bin at *my* fookin chair," he said.

Then the smallest, a mere baby of a man at sixteen stone, got to his feet and piped up, "Soomone's bin at *my* fookin chair an' all."

There broke out from the rest of the room a madrigal of lamentation; other people discovered that their cushions had bin fookin got at.

I was standing at the time, and was enthralled at the sight of bank robbers and murderers, pimps and extortionists, rapists and thieves, drug smugglers and terrorists, joined together thus, in common condemnation at the fiend who would, who could, commit so gross an act. They offered each other their respective cushions for inspection, in the manner of householders offering their houses for evaluation to other householders, in the aftermath of a hurricane, for mutual commiseration.

At that bubbling point when laughter becomes unsuppressible, it was stilled by a ghastly thought. Up to that moment I had enjoyed the diversion, and assumed it was not connected with me, or to any of the spheres in which I had influence. I tried to think calmly. The cushions, when they were virginal, were filled with a thick rectangular piece of grey green foam rubber; and where in the world I asked myself, had I quite recently heard that commodity being discussed. The answer came to me in the echoing phraseology of my partner, and with it a remembrance of the sly winking grimace he had formed.

"I got my own source for that," he had said. Good God I thought, and looked furtively around the assembled company of irate, cushion-wielding colleagues, to see if Joe was there. By now the extraneous substitutes were being pulled out of the cushions. The three uglies in the front row, holding their cushions like bags of crisps, were dipping in convulsively, and studying with intent curiosity and dismay as oily rags and waste denim from the weaver's shop fell at their feet. They gnashed their teeth and swore simple, horrible oaths of revenge against the culprit. If ever I saw a lynch mob that was it; and there, leading them verbally and rallying them to form vigilante groups was my forty per cent partner and work's manager, Mr Joe Fellatio, holding his own cushion somewhat histrionically aloft, I thought, to show transparently, that he too was a fellow sufferer. But I knew my work's manager rather too well to be fooled by red herrings like that. In fact it was that air of injured innocence that had convinced me of his guilt.

I hurried downstairs to my cell to write a few fervent good- bye letters, and make my will, composing on the way an epitaph that might suitably explain matters: "Cushioned to death in the cause of commerce". I visualized a teddy bear made of stone as my headstone.

A few minutes later Joe entered breathlessly giggling into the cell.

"Wah! That was close captain, weren't it," he said. "I thought they'd tumbled us then, didn't you?"

"You mean they haven't?"

"Course not. Whadd'you think, I'm stupid or what? Did you see how I double bluffed them with my own chair? Any way there's other blokes makin' teddies on the wing. Why's it got to be us whose done it?"

I had regained my composure; the situation did not look quite so disastrous.

"You keep using the first person plural in connection with this affair," I began. "It is not US at all. What you mean is *you*, you soppy bastard." I jabbed him forcefully where his chest would have been if he had stood still. "I'm not bothered one bit. It's got nothing to do with me. The foam rubber is entirely down to you. I'm only in charge of Sales and General policy. Destroying prison property is something I could not he associated with."

"Sixty per cent of the profits; sixty per cent of the whacks and smacks. Fair do's. Wish't I'd let you have seventy, now I come to think of it," he said in between spasms of hysterical laughter; seductive enough for me to abandon my pose and join him.

We decided to call an emergency board meeting then and there. Tea was made, and after a few appreciative sips I opened the proceedings as chairman, by congratulating the workforce on a reasonably profitable two week period. Joe applauded himself vigorously and said, "Up the workers." I then threw the meeting open to questions from the floor, and from the ensuing suggestions it emerged that the voters were unanimously in favour of destroying prison property, with the proviso that in future the company's agents should be more selective about whose chairs they plundered.

"In future the chairs of big, muscly, weighty people are to be left intact," I said.

"What sort of people are we looking for then, captain?" he asked.

"Small people."

"How small."

"Very small—midgets if possible."

"Pacifists?"

"They can be slightly larger."

A composite of the ideal sort of person whose cushion we could vandalize, gradually formed in our minds; a pacifist dwarf weakling, with no friends.

Joe said he would look out for such people on the wing, and the meeting was adjourned.

It was a parlous state of affairs for the company, and as more foam kept disappearing, the rumbles of discontent grew from the television room. Some guys were stripping their cushions off their chairs and taking them into their cells at night for safe keeping.

After another board meeting it was decided that I should get a friend to send a box of foam offcuts in to me. This was duly done, and when it arrived Joe displayed the box, nearly as tall as himself, in a prime position outside his door. The lid was left open, inviting passersby to observe that the contents were technicoloured, and not the drab green of the foam from the cushions.

The gossips and sleuths on the wing, who had Joe high up on the list as capable of being the dreaded cushion raider, now struck his name off, and disseminated the information that my work's manager could not be the one, as he had his own stock of foam.

Despite the legitimate foam we now owned, Joe used to carry out a lightning Viking raid on the cushions from time to time, just to keep his hand in.

From the start, business held steady at about one teddy a week. Apart from being in charge of sales, I was also voted in as the investments manager; a duty I undertook to the shareholders' satisfaction by regularly spending the profits on dope for the weekend. Having had an unnerving experience once, when he had been sold cinnamon powder and dough mixed together to imitate the texture of Lebanese, Joe was always full of praise for my ability to find the best that was available.

Inevitably, when there was dope to be smoked and tea to be drunk, board meetings were fait accompli. We had a period when methods of expansion and ways in which we could slander the quality and contents of teddy bears made by colleagues in the same business were discussed regularly.

Joe, brilliantly put it about, that if anyone interested chose to decapitate one of our rivals' teddies the identity of the cushion raider would be revealed. In short, we used the accepted advertising techniques that obtained in the wider world outside the Lazy L.

Chapter 13

The chance to change our one teddy a week image, was offered to us without warning by an exotic stranger from another land; a rotund and voluble West African with gold on his fingers, on his wrist, around his neck, and a further supply in his dentistry.

I had first met him in the Social Studies class, where along with the others including the teacher I had listened in mute bewilderment to his incomprehensible eloquence when he got excited, which he seemed to frequently do, in that class. At these times the fat on his cheeks and jowls shivered, and jellied, to the pitch of his feelings. Here and there discernible words such as 'Thad World' and 'Maggie Thatchah' and 'IMF' and 'revolooshun' gave us an inkling of the general drift of his tirade. The teacher, who was misplaced in his vocation, and should have been a senior member of the diplomatic service, used to nod intelligently in punctuation and say, "Quite so. Yes. Quite so," and then fearfully change the subject.

Our new customer had a flourishing African name which he seldom used, and was known as African George to most of us. A distinctive idiosyncrasy of speech made him memorable; it was, that he had imbued the consonant M with powers of expression that were manifold. He used that single letter elongated, and in different octaves, to suggest dissent or assent, encouragement or rejection, or mundanely, as an audible pause, while he thought of what to say next. I had heard him use it with inflections intimating derision, evaluation, condemnation, and wonderment, depending on the situation, with equal facility.

One Saturday afternoon on the playing fields, he rolled towards me, the extra weight around him quivering in sympathy with his forward motion. Despite his obesity it was apparent by his deportment that underneath that overlay of fat there was plenty of muscle.

"Ah! Krees, mmmm (elementary caution, exploratory.) I am interested to buy some mmmm teddy bahs," he said. I was instantly professional.

"I am interested to mmmm sell some teddy bahs, excellency," I replied. As a matter of business tactics, it is advisable to lob their idiom back to them, when dealing with foreign nationals—puts them at their ease; disarms them.

From under a tidily pruned upper lip he flashed some gold at me. "mmMMM," he said. (What have we here, clever Hindu gentleman?)

We mmmmed together courteously for a while, and I understood his requirements to be as follows. He wanted to commission six identical teddy bears. They had to be identical he said, as they were for the babas of influential relatives, and he did not want to show any preference among them for political reasons of his own. He gave me to understand that it was a delicate matter of keeping certain family relationships scrupulously balanced.

I gave him a solemn surety that my company was renowned for successfully undertaking such productions; and why, it was only the other day that the consulate of Nigeria had written in to congratulate mmmmm, etcetera.

"Lot of your people wakking mmmm in my country," he said.

"Quite so, quite so," I said, and hoped that my countrymen had not spoiled my pitch, by their reputation for beguiling innocent Africans in their souvenir shops, in his part of the world.

He said he had the cloth and was putting out some mmmmm tendahs. I told him that whereas my company did not normally undertake such small orders, it would do so to create good feelings between our two great nations.

He mmmed at me significantly on parting. I agreed to make my tender in a couple of days after consultation with my work's manager. The last mmmmm he had aimed at me was yoked to an observation, that in the past he had done a whole load of good business with Asians in Accra. If my deciphering was correct, there was contained in it an intonation that suggested I should watch my step; that he knew all about the smart arse moves some members of the Indian business community had pulled on Africans in the past.

When I told my work's manager that evening of this new development he punched the air ecstatically, and said we should call a board meeting right away. I agreed.

"This is a big un, so I better come with you on the next meet," he said. "I get on very well with Africans, tell 'em a few jokes about Idi Amin, and tickle 'em under the armpits. They love all that."

I began to see that what had sounded like a good idea, could have its drawbacks. If I took him with me, I would have to keep him muzzled.

"Don't start any of that nonsense with him," I warned. "This is an educated man, so don't give him any of that bullshit about talking to him in his own language either. Y'know what I mean. I makee, you buyee, chop chop, and all that crap. Leave the talking to me—just keep top lip and bottom lip buttoned together. And smarten up a bit, put some flowers in your hair, that sort of thing." We then discussed what we proposed to charge him; Joe suggesting perversely that since he was not British he should be liable for an extra tax, and I quelling that idea by advising him that if we were going to aspire to multinational status we should reject such protectionist policies. We concurred eventually, that since he was providing the cloth, I should try and get two pounds fifty per bear on a cash on delivery basis, and be prepared to go as low as two pounds each, but no lower. To make sure I could not grandly commit the company to an unprofitable contract, Joe said he would tag along, but keep his mouth shut throughout the negotiations.

Before we went out on exercise on the day we had agreed to meet, I made six cigarettes and put them in my tobacco tin together with an unsplit box of matches; an impressive show of financial stability.

"We got to show our prospective clients that they are not dealing with a cheapskate Johnny come lately firm," I said to Joe, who was currently engaged in trying to scratch some difficult to reach spot on his back.

Having taken to heart my admonition to make himself look presentable, he now looked as though he had dressed from a dustbin, standing in a waste tip—which was pretty good for him. His jeans had a patch on either knee, one of which had come unstitched, and hung like a giant scab from his leg; there were stains, hopefully egg, from breakfast on his T shirt, and on his head, constantly adjusting it, he wore a blue peaked cap made in the weaver's shop. It had a simple transfer message ironed above the bridge of the peak. It said, "Piss off". From under his cap like trailing seaweed, his hair hung in strands down to his shoulders.

"How's the Spanish comin' on, captain?" he asked, grinning crookedly.

"Slow and steady," I said.

"Learned any swear words yet? Som'ing right vommitty and insulting?"

"I know how to say son of a whore in Spanish," I said guardedly.

"Nothing worse than that?"

"No. What are you asking for? So you can start using it on me, I suppose. You must think I came over on the last banana boat. Do you know that if you had a sack of coal on your back you wouldn't need any make up to play Quasimodo."

"That's the straw that broke the camel's back," he cackled briefly. "Go on, tell us it."

"Tell you what?"

"How to say son of a prostitute?"

"Is there anything in your life that is sacred?" I asked.

"Nothing whatsoever," he replied.

"In that case, if you utter a solemn promise on nothing whatsoever that I shall never use the foul oath I am about to hear, on my honourable friend and chairman of the company, Senor Kris."

All this was taking place in the corridors leading to the double electronic gates that opened out on to the playing fields. There was quite a lot of pedestrian traffic at that time of the evening; mostly guys in shorts and singlets going for a run or a kick about with a football. Most of them knew us, and skirted round the posed reciting Joe, or tried to grab the cap out of his hand in passing. There was a sudden urgent pandemonium of thudding feet, and a herd of intense, grim faced men in studded boots, smelling of wintergreen, swept round a corner, and knocked him over. It was the prison rugby squad out for a practice, ever hopeful that they might catch the Governor's eye.

"Bunch of fucking poofs," Joe shouted after them, feeling around for bruises. "That's all they are. That's all they play the game for; to grope each other's bollocks in the scrum. I've seen 'em. That's how they get their jollies."

He straightened his cap to the tilt that pleased him most in the reflection of a window, and I made him take it off again, to continue with the oath-taking ceremony.

"Hardly worth it," he grumbled.

"That's up to you my friend," I said. "If you want another language at your command, and not just any language, but the language of Cervantes and Lorca, certain rituals have to be observed."

After he had sworn that he would exempt me from the invective, and after I had insisted on a couple of repeats just to be sure, I told him how to say son of a whore in Spanish. It pleased him greatly. He tried it on his image in another window, and on the library officer, locking up for the night. The next time he used it was on the uniformed figures counting the prisoners at the electronic gates, as they trickled through on to the playing fields.

Much as I applauded his choice of professions on whom to try out these words, I kept a prudent pace or two away from him, with my mouth clearly closed, so that any Spanish-speaking member of Her Majesty's prison officers would know where to direct his attention.

This is in the best textbook tradition of chairmanship; we are simply policy makers. It is always the junior executives of the company who have to expose themselves to the hazards that may accompany the implementation of those policies.

There were no Spanish speaking personnel about that evening, and we passed uneventfully on to the playing fields. Having no one to insult for a few minutes Joe shouted 'Hijo de puta' to the sky a few times.

Most of the attention was focused on the football pitch where an inter-wing match was in progress. The players were performing with unusual gusto, and we surmised that a fair bit of silver was riding on the outcome.

When African George joined us he wrinkled his nose, pouted his lips, and made it clear to me sotto voce that he did not hold my works manager in high esteem.

"He is the one mmmm who makes shit packages, and throws them from his window," he said, pointing his jowls in Joe's direction, who at that moment was practising his Spanish on the umpire.

"I beg your pardon," I said. Company chairmen with any gumption, make at least a token effort to defend their company servants.

"Yes, mmm," (distasteful frown and deprecatory inflection) "he is the one, makes them and throws them from his window. Officah told me. Yes, mmmmm."

"Officah would," I said, realizing not for the first time that the reputation my work's manager had earned himself in another prison was being distorted. I guided George by pressure on elbow towards the rugby field. I knew that if Joe heard George's opinion of him we would lose the contract, and George would have his dignity shaved drastically.

"He's not one of them," I said. "He lives on the ground floor; and as you probably know such people like to live at least three floors up, so that they can hear and see their projectiles when they land."

I then told him the story of Joe's activities at the other prison, which may have led to the misunderstanding. It was this. When Joe began his five-year sentence for burglary, he was held at a local prison; there, for not falling into line with the regime, he incurred the general animosity of the prison officers, and became the special interest of one of them. This man took it upon himself to hound Joe into conformity. It became an evangelical mission with this officer to try and squeeze all the impudence and cheek out of the little man's personality. After he had been placed on report several times, lost remission, and spent a considerable number of days in the punishment block, Joe decided to reward the officer with a special decoration.

Accordingly, he gathered up his excreta for a day or two in a newspaper; took it to the mailbag shop where he worked, and where also the officer would be on duty, sitting sovereign on a dais that overlooked the prisoners as they sewed.

He jumped up behind the officer and gave him a prolonged faecal facial with the newspaper. The officer did not like that one little bit. He acquired a new nickname; from that day on he was known as shitface.

Before Joe was transferred from that prison, his five-year-sentence had grown to seven. A send-off truncheon party organized by colleagues of the contaminated officer, and to which he was ethically not invited, ensured that Joe walked with a slight limp, due to a chipped bone in his ankle, from that day on.

"Sooner limp a little, than be called shitface all your life, eh, captain?" Joe had cackled at me once.

African George was mmmming away in my ear like an industrious bee; the tone varying occasionally to express respect or approval for Joe's behaviour, and sinking to the lower registers in a sympathetic rumble when he heard how Joe ended up with a limp.

He accepted my suggestion that to regain corporate face over the incident, the officers would try to discredit Joe as an indiscriminate hurler of excreta wrapped in newspapers, known in prison vernacular as shit parcels, rather than as a small, one hundred and ten pound, five foot nothing heroic figure on a singular mission of revenge. There are those who wear the trappings of authority who cannot accept, despite all the historical evidence to the contrary, that there are some human beings whose spirit can only be quenched by physical death.

Having adequately defended my works manager's credentials, I began to think of suitable words with which to change the subject nonchalantly to the topic of teddy bear sales. At this point Joe joined us; also at this point, a light wind blew over the prison, and wafted the rotting smell of the manure used by the adjoining farm into our nostrils.

Somewhat over-defensively I pointed out to George that the smell was not Joe; that it had blown in from the outside world, with pantomimic hand gestures to indicate the direction of the wind.

He received this with an unconvinced mmmm; and his interest in the matter of sewage disposal was reawakened

"But who are these mmmm dahty people who do this?" he asked.

Joe, sworn to silence, maintained it. I reasoned that it would help the sale of our products if the chairman appeared knowledgeable about other subjects, to present myself as an intellectual, prone to academic enquiry.

"They are a secret religious fertility cult called dejectaphiles," I said. "Predominantly part of the prison tradition, although the phenomena has occasionally surfaced among the high rise tribes in the big cities of Britain. I have personally seen some evidence in lifts and landings in the tall concrete boxes that these backward people live in.

The subject has been made somewhat cloudy because of the erroneous belief that it is caused by necessity, which may be true in local prisons where the toilet facilities are nominal; and the time allowed to use them negligible, but in a place like this there is no need for it. One must assume that it is a matter of preference. This view is confirmed when one examines the logistics involved. First a newspaper, and incidentally, the purist will only use the Sun or News of the World newspapers as most closely related to their contents, must be spread on the floor, or bed, or other suitable platform; the perpetrator must then lower his trousers, squat over and evacuate on to it. He has then to wrap it up in the ritual way so that it will burst on impact for maximum spread, and hurl it from his window with a sideways motion, so that it lands under his neighbour's windows, thereby disguising the source from where it was presented to the world. If his cell is located in a position that allows him to pitch it on to the exercise yard or a concrete path it must be regarded as a bonus. The dejectaphile derives extra comfort from witnessing the curious high stepping mannerisms his colleagues affect, to get past the area he has territorially staked out."

George was mmmmming intently in my ear; Joe was strumming the difficult to reach spot on his back, and occasionally practising his Spanish pleasantry en passant, on people who displeased him.

"How do you know mmmm so much of these people?" George asked.

Joe sniggered; I quelled it with a chairman's look. He went back to his Spanish. I surmised that all the urbane good manners and subtleties of custom that attend the business of buying and selling East of the Suez would have to be brought into play at this meeting: the primary reason that we were there for had to be avoided. I had to engender a mood of cordiality first, or find some cause to which we were mutually sympathetic. My erudite chairman's mind saw an opening and took it.

"I first became interested in dejectaphiles while I was writing my thesis for a doctorate in landing cleanersip. The specialist subject was latrines and urinals, and as you may well suppose there is a plethora of printed matter on the subject. Here and there, concealed in the small print of footnotes and reference indices I came across the word, and decided to conduct my own survey. I have to admit that these people guard information about their identities so zealously that I have never actually met anyone who would look me in the eye and say, I am a dejectaphile, and proud of it. Even more perplexing was the fact that no one knew for certain which of his neighbours was one. Incidentally, their creations are called shit parcels, and not packages; a linguistic quibble I know, but package suggests something of more robust construction. Don't you agree?"

"Mmmmm," African George mused.

"The other school of thought," I continued, "is that it is linked to British Colonial history."

At the words British Colonial history, George began to fight for air, and show all the signs of a man with something passionate to say. I continued.

"Having been engaged for a few hundred years in spreading civilisation, a euphemism in general terms for shitting on the peoples of far off exotic places, the British, finding their pastime denied them, have produced this freak social behaviour not unlike the hallucinatory symptoms that accompany the withdrawal from a drug like—"

All the air George had been storing up in short gasps was suddenly released in a torrent; and when it was analyzed, this is what it said.

"mmmmm, gudda budda wudda Heathrow Airport mmm wudda budda gudda transit, mmm gudda budda prison; dahty peepul, gudda mmmm budda; ah! imperialist budda wudda Maggie Thatchah mmm budda wudda social structah!"

My work's manager who had never encountered an African George in full verbal flood before, showed his bewilderment by ceasing to scratch his back, and reciting his Spanish.

"What's he sayin', is he 'avin' a go at us," he asked.

"Ashanti," I hissed through a mouth pointed sideways. "Mouth shut, ears open. Listen and learn. Scholarly talk, don't interrupt. Very delicate stage of negotiations."

"You could have fooled me," Joe said, as George rumbled on, oblivious to our incomprehension.

When he had finished I said, "Quite so. Absolutely. Quite so," and translated his excitement to Joe.

"He says," I said, offering my tobacco tin around yet again, "that he had passed through Britain several times before, but had never stayed longer than the time it took to change planes at Heathrow. This time, through a prior signal from a dissatisfied colleague, he was welcomed heartily in the transit lounge by Customs officers who went without hesitation to one particular suitcase, and the concealed contents of some wooden face masks, ensured that he walks about here with us today."

I then filled in some other bits of George's prison history that I already knew; how when he was on remand he was spontaneously approached by a fellow prisoner who suggested very persuasively that for a suitable fee, he would kill the chief, and only prosecution witness, at George's trial; the same man who had betrayed him to the Customs. George it seems, welcomed this proposal as an elegant solution to his problems. Money was paid when he got out on bail, to this man. On subsequent visits to see George at the remand prison, he brought with him another man who he said was more versatile in the techniques of killing people.

After a few meetings George lost heart for the venture and wanted to call the whole thing off. Hitman two was insistent, even threatening, that it was too late to pull out; that all the guns, and garottes, and other paraphernalia for dismemberment had been bought; quicklime pits dug, and acid baths prepared. George was persuaded to change his mind back again. It was this aspect of the case that peeved him, still peeved him most, four years later as he walked with us.

When George finally came to trial he faced two charges; the first, the lesser one concerning narcotics, and the other more serious charges of attempted murder, attempting to pervert the course of justice, and so on.

The truth of the matter was that Hitman one was in fact a con-man desperately trying to find mitigation on a bank fraud charge he was facing. He conceived the idea of suggesting a crime to a fellow inmate, with the sole intention of getting him caught. To aid him in this criminal plan he had the cooperation of the country; it will come as no surprise that hired assassin number two, the man who had spoken so plausibly of the methods and venues of murder, was a policeman with a tape recorder in his briefcase.

George learned two new words from the barrister who defended him; words which make him wince, pucker his face into contortions of loathing and anger: they are, agent provocateur.

He got two years on the first charge and a further seven for the second. The man who conceived the plot found the charges he faced attenuated, and walked away from court with a suspended sentence. The judge commended him on his help to the police on an unrelated serious crime.

"George says," I continued, "that he has reconciled himself to all that, and has kept himself occupied in prison, which is the only part of this illustrious country apart from Heathrow Airport that he has ever seen, by studying the social and political structure of his hosts. He is not very impressed; and for reasons which are some what gudda wudda obscure, he does not think too highly of Margaret Thatcher either. The other matter that disturbs him are the shit parcels that come whistling down past his window at night. He cannot comprehend, and neither can I, why anyone who is able to use conventional toilet facilities at any time of the night should do this. As you heard I tried to enlighten him on the subject."

After several other matters including the agricultural policy of the Marxist third world, and the system of naming children by the day of the week they were born on, among the Ashanti people, had been dispensed with, and finding ourselves in agreement on everything, we moved gracefully without contrivance on to teddy bears, in the way practised businessmen negotiate contracts. He said that if our company was going to make them, he would have to take delivery of all six in two weeks time—would that be a problem?

"No problem," I assured him.

Joe had a coughing and spluttering fit; fragments of his one line in Spanish spewed out. I gave him a malicious and mighty whack on the back as first aid.

"Thanks, captain, I needed that," he said, then turning to George.

"How much?" he barked.

"What he is asking, Excellency, in his crude avaricious way," I intervened, "is whether you will be paying by cash, hire purchase agreement, or Barclaycard. You see our company has different answers to each one of those arrangements."

"Cash only, with me," George said. "I have no mmm shortage of funds."

I made spurious calculatory sounds in my throat, suggesting I was engaged in a costing operation, where data such as the level of inflation, incipient worker recalcitrance, and the cost of tea bags to keep the worker fortified, had to be evaluated.

"Two pounds fifty per unit, that's fifteen pounds altogether, delivered within fourteen days," I said shakily. African George said, 'mm mmmm' and waddled off in the direction of the outside toilets.

"What the fuck does that mean?" Joe asked.

"Ashanti is a devilishly clever language," I explained. "One of its less complicated facets is that it only has one letter in its alphabet. It follows therefore, that how you mmm is crucial. Did you for instance make note of the sharp epiglottal thrust of the second m of the first word, no; or further, did you record the enormous vibrato in the third m of the second word, no; or even how neatly, one could say surgically, it was arrested in the fourth, no?"

"I missed all that captain, I thought he said mm mmmm and fucked off," Joe said. "I've only just mastered Spanish. Good job you're such an expert in the lingo. So what did he say?"

"He said," I said, "What do these two, this filthy degenerate Englishman, and the wily smiley Eastern Tandoori merchant take me for. Do they think they are dealing with a starstruck African from the bush. By the beard of Chaka the Great, I have a mind to go take a piss, letting them think I am not interested. They are quite clearly broke, notwithstanding the flashy gesture of the tobacco tin. It didn't escape me that the filthy one gasped in surprise and tried to take two, and was smacked on the wrist by wily smiley, as he was offering them around: I think, big daddy George gonna make them two clever bastards sweat a while."

"So what do you reckon," Joe asked.

"I think he'll come back and by the orthodox rules of bargaining offer us half," I said.

I was palpably wrong. As we spoke, the doorway to the toilet was blocked briefly by George's great bulk; then he turned towards us purposefully.

He was about five yards away and bearing down fast, when Joe made a seemingly irrelevant but remarkable statement; a statement, which he claimed later at the board meeting that night, had turned the tide in our favour.

Establishing a firm eye contact with the approaching George he said, "Aiy, Maggie Thatcher," then producing farting noises with his lips, he pinched his nose with the fingers of one hand, while he pulled an imaginary chain with the other. George appeared nonplused for a few seconds, then understanding transformed his face into a wide gold capped smile, which led in turn to a high-pitched uncontrollable giggle, as Joe did it again. That George had found the mime apposite became evident a few seconds later, when he reproduced it for our approval, laughing even louder at his own rendition. It appeared that Joe had managed to encapsulate all the sentiments he had wished to express on the lady in a single audio-visual phrase.

Thereafter wherever they met, in the corridors or the canteen

110

queue or on their way to work, they pronounced on Mrs Thatcher within the interpretive boundaries of this single expression.

"Ah! Krees," he said finally, mopping his face with a crisp folded white handkerchief, "your friend is a good man."

"One of the best," I said. Joe smirked contentedly. "What I mmmm propose is this." He exposed a fleshy pink palm to the sky; in it nestling comfortably, was a twenty pound note, folded to the dimensions of a postage stamp.

"I do not wish to mmm bargain in this mattah because you are a gentleman mmmm like myself. I am willing to pay this," he shook his hand, and the sovereign's profile emphasized the movement, "for six teddy bahs. I cannot mmmmm make a bettah offah."

The prevalent rate of exchange was twelve pounds of usable silver for a twenty pound note. It was a remarkably acceptable offer. I was about to agree graciously that yes, bargaining was unbecoming between men of rank and distinction, and anyway should not be conducted in the presence of a subordinate native, when the subordinate native's dirty fingernailed hand struck out like a cobra in front of me at the tantalizing target in George's palm.

"Done. It's a deal." Joe was rapturously kissing and murmuring endearments to it; I had to exert considerable pressure on his wrist and right ear, before he would let it go.

I handed it back to George, on the understanding that it would be ours to kiss and caress, after we had delivered four of the six teddy bahs.

We parted good friends; George and Joe did a few Maggie Thatcher's on the way back to our respective wings, and even tried a duet but their timing on the audible effects was not satisfactory. Even the chairman, I have to admit did a couple, and found them psychologically satisfying. Credit was speedily arranged for a dope purchase against the collateral of the twenty pound note, and we had a celebratory board meeting. We expressed, each in our turn, how well we had negotiated the contract.

"It was me that come in with the coop de grass at the end there," Joe said.

I reminded him that it was my donnish discourse on excreta that had created the air of conviviality, necessary at these meetings. We were however, in agreement that we made a good team at the negotiating table.

The only imponderability now was whether George would change his mind between then and lunch time on the day after; by arrangement, I was to meet him at the door of his wing to get the cloth.

When I got there the following day, George not only gave me the cloth, but with a flourish shook hands with me. I felt the unexpected texture of folded paper in my palm, and slipped it into my pocket.

"We are gentlemen, we can mmm have trust in each othah. I have made payment in advance," he said.

He gave me a Maggie Thatcher, and I gave him one back, as recent company vogue demanded, before I left.

My work's manager, after a few seconds of initial shock, when I showed him the twenty pound note, summarized our feelings exactly.

"What a scholar and bloody gentleman the man is," he said.

I couldn't better that expression, so took it as a lead to imbue my work's manager by guileful invention of a proposed further order of six teddies, by the same buyer if the first six were satisfactory with the appropriate dedication to the task ahead.

"Only the best captain," Joe assured me. "It's only what the bloke deserves, payin' up front like that."

"British craftsmanship," I ventured.

"All the way. Nothing but the best for our customer from the dark continent, eh! captain."

"When our products are being dandled in the great lounges and salons of Accra," I said, as a company chairman with distant dreams would, "I want to hear people say, by Gad there's a British bear. You hear me. Never forget you're British, my boy."

"Never, captain. Thin red line of Empire, captain."

"Absolutely."

"Captain?"

"Yes?"

"Would you mind fuckin' off now, an' gettin' some illegal substances with the profits, or we'll 'ave nothin' for the board meeting this evening."

So I went to do what company chairmen enjoy doing most.

Chapter 14

It took two days of rigorous board meetings to realise that I had blundered crassly; I should not have shown Joe the twenty pound note. Now that dope was plentiful, and board meetings convened for the flimsiest reasons, his earlier affirmation about a steadfast and determined work pattern was forgotten. I was offered various degrees of mañana as placation, whenever I suggested that he got started.

These ranged from an energetic, "I'm startin' on it as soon as we are banged up at five o'clock", to a languid, totally unconvincing, "You worry too much, I've got everythin' under control."

The matter was finally brought to a head at an acrimonious board meeting. It was suggested without any sense of sacrilege at this meeting, that seeing as how time was getting short, the chairman of the company would have to roll his sleeves up and work. Needless to say, I told the presumptuous fool to refer to clause 3b subsection F of the union rules that regulates the activity, or lack of it, of chairmen. His response was typical of the pampered worker of the 20th century, when faced by reason and logic.

"Bollocks," he said.

"Would you care to rephrase that?" I enquired.

"Yeah. Bolll-llocks. I ain't doin' six bleedin' teddies on my tod, and that's that. I'll need some help."

"Well, get some help then," I shrieked, with an impetuosity spurred on by the retreating spectre of work. "But mind," I added hastily, "You get a good man. Not another wanker like you."

"What we're lookin' for," he mused, is a strong, stupid, stout fellow, to do the work, while we discuss important matters at board meetings."

I listened aghast at this blatant plagiarism. This was chairman's talk coming from the mouth of a lowly worker.

"Got just the bloke for it, as it goes," he said.

"Who?"

"You'll see. A deserving case, ex-Gurkha, British to the core, same as us."

"Oh, my God," I said.

At this stage of the narrative, it behoves me to describe in some detail, the man my work's manager chose to be his assistant. I do so, only to illustrate how tradition was maintained in our company. Joe exhibited in his choice, all the business intelligence I had shown, when I picked him to be the work's manager, of our company.

The new man's name was Charlie, but he was never called that. It was either Snowy—his hair; Shaky—his hands; or that slippery old bastard—his disposition.

He was a small wiry man, and at sixty eight the oldest inmate on the wing. He had a quick birdlike manner, which kept him looking busy when he was not doing anything constructive. He was nearly always dressed in overalls, and prison issue striped blue shirt, several sizes too big for him. His face and hands gave the impression of shop soiled-pieces of ivory, smoothed and rolled by a thousand inquisitive customers.

When he was asked what his job was in prison, he had a baffling answer. "See them stairs over there," he would say, raising his arm at an angle of forty five degrees in any haphazard direction, left or right, that pleased him. "I doos them twice a day." At these times he contrived to look utterly exhausted, as though the task was daily becoming too much for him.

It was commonly accepted that the stairs only existed in his imagination.

A small agile man for his age, with milky blue eyes, that darted everywhere as he spoke; and he spoke habitually from the side of his mouth, furtively, even when commenting on the weather, as though he was passing through a hostile locality where arrest was imminent. He had cause to feel apprehensive, having spent thirty three of his sixty eight years on earth in penal institutions, civilian and military.

His sentences, the longest of which had been eight years, were of types that were only legend to the rest of us. He introduced us to words whose practical application we were thankful never to have experienced.His memory had stored them in mothballed initials: H.L. (hard labour): P.D. (Preventive Detention): P.S. (Penal servitude): E.S. (Extended sentence). He spoke also of punishments that are no longer used; bread and water, and the specialist punishment of having to do everything at the double. The one he remembers most clearly, is the one he calls the dustbin routine; the psychologically debilitating task of cleaning a dustbin with carbolic soap and sandstone until it gleamed, knowing that it was going to get filled up with slops in a few hours, and knowing also, that the same cleaning chore would be given to him the next day; a failure to accomplish which, to the required standard of reflective brilliance, would result in three days Number one.

"Oh, aye," he would say lugubriously, "Number one. Bread and water for three days," the rills on his face, the colour of a faded covenant, growing deeper.

These memories evoke no bitterness or regret now, only a sort of bewildered wonderment at his own life, which he expressed with a scratch at the pure white, threadbare coverlet, on his head, as he grins toothlessly, exposing baby pink gums.

He was conscripted into the army at the outbreak of war, having, that precise day come out of prison. The address of an office to report to was given to him. He failed to report. Six months later, recently emergent from a military prison, he was given the address of the same office to report to. He failed to report.This sequence of events with a few incursions into civilian prisons ensured that he kept himself out of the war for its whole duration.

"I don't 'ave nothing to do with politics and all things like that," he says. "I didn't want to soldier, and that were the end of it. Why should I shoot at them German blokes? They done nothing to me, an' some of them was conscripts same as me. Why don't Churchill and Hitler and Chamberlain and all people like that fight it out amongst themselves? I don't want to kill no one. Never 'ave."

By what convoluted reasoning my work's manager could have described him as an ex-Gurkha, I never found out. He had perfected the knack of looking industrious at all times, and only close attention to what he was achieving showed that his endeavours had no purpose or end.

Charlie-watching was a beguiling pastime for some of us, as we waited in the partitioned kitchen for the kettle to boil.

He had a few props that helped: a mop, a tin of scouring powder, a few cleaning rags overflowing from overall pockets, and into which he blew his nose from time to time inspecting the outcome before he stuffed them back. With these, mumbling and moving about from place to place, he produced the effect of being at work, perfectly. A customary pattern of behaviour would bring him out of his cell carrying his mop, which he would prop behind the boiler; then back to his cell to get the tin of scouring powder; to be followed by a fruitless search for a mythical mop bucket for half an hour, which he claims he left, "right there a minute ago an' someone's nicked it". When he asks people if they have seen it, it is with the air of a man desperately trying to get to work, but being hindered in that objective at every turn. Unable to trace the whereabouts of the mop bucket he adjourns for tea, which could take an indeterminate length of time, for he is a man who likes to grab a quick snooze whenever he can. Later, he comes back to move the mop from behind the boiler to the recess area; on his way back, he gets the rags out of his pocket and energetically rubs a nonexistent stain on the draining board for a few seconds. Then looking virtuously workworn, he goes back to his cell with his virgin mop in hand.

One of the highlights of his day is helping the regular cleaners bring in the food trolley from the kitchen. He is invariably a hindrance, but the cleaners don't object; they know Charlie is on his scavenging, and shoplifting expedition. While the food trolleys are being loaded; a task that perforce involves a certain amount of confusion, as the various diets are checked, he slips away to see what he can cadge or steal. Usually a couple of onions or half a small cabbage find their way into the bottom of his capacious overall pockets, under the cleaning rags. These he later barters for tobacco or teabags with other prisoners who do a bit of home cooking. He has been banned from the kitchen on more than one occasion, but he somehow manages to worm his way back in again.

Yet, it was not for these attributes that Charlie was memorable. That, was due to the reason why he had been given his other nickname: Shaky.

He shook. That is to say, he jerked. That is to say, he trembled all his conscious hours. Most of the time his hands and arms vibrated in a noticeable shudder. This relatively conservative rhythm gave way to something more spectacular when he had one of his attacks, which happened about twice a day. When this took place, it seemed as if he were the recipient of a series of slight electric shocks. A deranged puppeteer took over the upper part of his body; his hands would flop up and down like broken winged birds, while efforts to hold down one leaping hand with the other produced an effect so dramatic and startling that when I first saw it, I thought the whole performance was feigned. When the spasm passed, "it's a what soma callit syndrome," he would say. There was in the way he announced that, a hint of proprietorial pride.

This disability has classified him unfit for labour in the shops. The regular officers on the wing know by experience not to entrust him with any job that could, by any elasticity of imagination, produce an accident. They are reminded of the time when Shaky, in the act of putting out a small fire in a metal bin, nearly burned the kitchen down and the time when given the task of keeping the boiler topped up, he flooded the place out.

Reflecting on his army non-career, I could not understand how any organized group of combatants, especially one as illustrious as the British army, could possibly want such a man in their ranks, constituting as he surely would have done, a graver danger to his own side than the enemy.

It was this man of dubious mobility, this grand master of skivers, this geriatric blunderer, this prince of ineffectual endeavour, that my work's manager chose to be his assistant.

So it was that the spirit and continuity of tradition within our company was maintained.

Chapter 15

"If you stand there, watchin' 'im like that, you'll make him nervous, an' he'll 'ave one of his what-soma-callits and the flow of production will stop," Joe said.

I stood captivated, mouth open, at the sight.

Earlier that day, I had bumped into African George on my way back from the gym, and in the course of a statutory progress report told a few substantial untruths; I told him that work on his teddy bahs was progressing at unbelievable speed, and impelled by the motion of that first one, went on to say that I was personally supervising the whole operation.

"Indian people are very good for business," African George said. "Very had wakkers."

"Quite so, tremendous," I agreed bravely.

I am by nature a believer in miracles. We exchanged Maggie Thatchahs, and a psychologist of average perception would have noted that mine lacked conviction.

I hurried back to the wing, one defeatist scheme being replaced by another, in my head. Some idea of the general drift of my thoughts may be indicated, by just one of the courses of action I was contemplating. I would set fire to my bed, with a few bits of foam rubber, and fur fabric, on top, in case of any postmortem verdicts. I imagined facing African George the next day explaining the catastrophe, touching in my mind's eye the black armband, or preferably six little armlets; a cenotaph to the teddy bahs that had been cremated. So vividly did I visualize this scene, that I heard myself saying, that in spite of this calamity, being an honourable businessman, I would make full recompense as soon as my company was reformed.

It was reasonable therefore, for me to stand in the doorway of Joe's cell in a state of pleasurable shock. "Well, I never," I said disbelievingly. "Is this for real. I'm not dreaming am I?"

Shaky was sitting on the floor, leaning against the bed. A dead rollup thin as a match, was stuck to his upper lip. On one side of his outstretched legs there was a cardboard box of foam rubber pieces; and on his lap like a turkey waiting to be stuffed on a kitchen table, there lay the carcase of a teddy, with a slit up its middle. Into that opening Shaky was shovelling, and thumbing in, foam pieces as fast as his shake would allow him. True, a lot of the pieces were missing the slit completely and spilling out over his knees, but enough were getting through to make a significant difference to the emerging shape of the teddy. It was a case of two steps forward, one step back. He was working at a nervous, feverish pace.

"He can't keep that speed up for long, can he?" I asked.

"'Course he can. That's just his second gear. You want to see him when he is going flat out. He's like a blur. Told you didn't I? Ex-Gurkha, used to jungle warfare."

"By God! I think you're right," I agreed.

Over the next two days I was reduced from chairman to teaboy in the company hierarchy, while Joe reclined on his bed with his foot within distance of the vibrating Shaky. It was geographically situated thus, so that at the merest hint of Shaky slowing down Joe would liven him up with a prod of his toe.

Before my image as the teamaker became a fixed fact of company structure, I brought the matter up.

"How about you making the tea for a change?" I asked.

Joe at that moment was studying the Racing News, smelly stockinged foot extended in the direction of Shaky's shoulder blades.

He looked up, startled. "What?"

"You heard what I said."

"If I make the tea, you reckon you can mind the old cunt do you? If he 'aves one of his what-soma-callits you reckon you can revive him with the kiss of life do you? Well, do you?"

I looked at Shaky's shuddering profile and the glistening, unsniffed-up upper lip.

"I think I'll make some tea," I said. "I guess you boys must be thirsty. And by the way I don't think you need to give him the kiss of life if he flakes out. Just wave your foot over his nose. I assure you, that has the power to bring an Egyptian mummy back to life."

Shaky's jaw fell open like a hinged trap door, and he emitted a high-pitched whinnying laugh.

"Shadaap," Joe said, and prodded him with his toe. "It weren't that funny. Get stuffin'."

Shaky hooked up his jaw, and went back to work.

It was during my temporary role as teamaker that the request for something a bit stronger for Shaky was made yet again. Over the preceding two days I had learned of the conditions under which Shaky had accepted the position as Emergency Stuffer in our Company. The initial offer had been, that at the end of his stint, he was to receive one ounce of tobacco, and a one pound deal of dope. He had argued that dope was sinful; illegal, and he had read in the *Readers Digest* that after two weeks on it one turned into a raving poofter. He said he would settle for a gallon of hooch instead. That suited me, as Mac the Brew had an embarrassing excess of the stuff, and said he would trade a gallon for a one pound deal of dope.

Now the hints were becoming demands, that a token interim payment, a show of good faith, should be made; Joe acting as Shaky's spokesman.

"Have a heart, captain," Joe said. "The poor old bugger 'as been workin' 'is fingers to the bone. A couple of mugs of the hard stuff would put some lead in his pencil, not to mention sparkle in his eyes. Know what I mean?"

I had originally resolved not to make any interim payments to my workforce, but these seemed exceptional circumstances.

In the two days Shaky had been working he had stuffed four bears; Joe put in the final sutures, and fluffed up the fur around the incision with a wire brush, so that the scar would not show.

African George took the look-a-like quads into his arms, giving each one a punch on the nose, and another on the bum, presumably a Ghanaian show of proprietorship, and pronounced them acceptable.

"Personal supervision. Nothing like it to keep the workers on their toes," I said.

" Indian people very good for business," he said. "Very had wakkers."

"Oh, fantastic!" I agreed virtuously. I showed him some calluses on my palm, evidence of the way I held the badminton racquet.

"Caused by pushing the needle through heavy material while instructing my apprentices," I said.

I had come away from our meeting feeling quite satisfied at the way the teddy bear operation was proceeding. Strong leadership, decisive planning, and picking one's workers with care had paid off. It was in that last clause that I felt especially gratified. Only a chairman of great acuity could have perceived that in such unpromising raw material as Shaky had been, there was a master stuffer of soft toys waiting to be liberated. I had a mind to write a letter to the Home Secretary informing him that I had singlehanded instigated the first genuine case of rehabilitation in a British prison. I had taken a wilful, and deviant personality, a man terrified of work, and turned him into a skilled craftsman of honour, and commitment.

It was an amalgam of these thoughts that persuaded me to change my mind about an interim show of goodwill. Accordingly, that evening, I deposited in Joe's cell a one gallon detergent plastic container full of hooch. Mac the Brew had warned me of its taste and potency.

"Watch out for that stuff," I said. "Mac says it tastes like shampoo, and kicks like a mule."

"That's just how the old bugger likes it," Joe said. "I think I'll ration him to two mugs a night."

I left them doing an alcoholic jig around the plastic container, swearing eternal devotion and respect to company and chairman.

That evening they were not visible in the public places of entertainment on the wing. At some point in the evening I heard Shaky's querulous voice attempting to reproduce the songs that had been popular in his youth: Bing Crosby and Paul Robeson classics, and a medley of hymns. I heard also, that when the effect of the hooch was at its most invigorating, he had offered to fight anyone in the prison, over fifteen rounds.

At lunchtime the following day I breezed into Joe's cell to pick up the last two teddies one day ahead of schedule. Joe's face and Shaky's absence hinted darkly that all was not well in the company.

"What's up?" I asked.

"The old cunt's out of the game, that's what," Joe said.

"What do you mean, out of the game? What the hell does that mean?"

"Tom and Dick."

"Never mind the regional affectations. What are you trying to say."

"I'm tryin' to say," Joe said patiently, "that, on account of the slippery old bastard tippin' the contents of a gallon container of 'ighly volatile mixture down 'is Gregory, he is now Tom and Dick. Got that."

"Well, how much did he have?"

"The whole bleedin' gallon. I got two small teacups out of it, and that was my lot. He guzzled the rest."

"I thought you said you were going to ration him to two mugs?"

"'Course I did. I'm not stupid, y'know," Joe said peevishly. "But the slippery old sod must 'ave seen me stash the rest under me bed, an' come back in when I was out 'avin a puff and nicked it. He left the bottle behind with a thimblefull at the bottom. Must 'ave poured the rest into a jug and took it with him."

"Jesus," I exclaimed. "I had a taste of that stuff. There was enough there to kill a crocodile."

"Well, he ain't dead. Didn'tcha 'ear 'im singin' and bawlin' last night. Says he was 'allucinatin', an' spoke to his mum an' dad who died twenty year ago."

"Anyway, that was last night," I said curtly. It was clear to me that a chairman's incisive approach to the crisis was needed.

"Hasn't he been told," I asked, "that company regulations do not, I repeat, do not, allow for workers being Tom and Gregory on a working day?"

"Just a minute, captain. I want you to get all this right in your head. He's not Tom and Gregory at all. His Gregory is a bit sore after all the 'O come all ye faithfuls' he done last night, but all in all it's still in one piece and workin'. He's Tom and Dick. Sick. Get it? Gregory Peck, neck. Simple when you know how it works."

"I'm sorry," I said "my English was channelled to me through Macaulay & Gibbon. But whatever delinquent linguistics one wishes to use, we are as a company on Red Alert, are we not?"

Joe agreed that that was indeed the case. "Well, we better get cracking, put our shoulders to the wheel, and get stuck in (all useful phrases for non-working chairman) and finish the job. Tomorrow is the deadline day."

"We? Did I hear you say *we*, Captain?"

"Certainly I said *we*," I replied. "You musn't make the mistake of thinking that because I am chairman of the company and exude urbanity and sophistication, I am incapable of strenuous work. I am perfectly willing to sit here and prod you with my toe, while you finish off the contract."

"Let's 'ave a board meeting at six after bang up, to size up the situation, eh? There's only one and a bit left to do. I can knock them off in no time at all tonight. Everythin's under control."

So of course we held a board meeting that evening. Joe had constructed an unusual smoking device, halfway between a bong and a chillum, out of an empty shampoo bottle and a carrot. In it we tested some Jamaican grass that had recently hit the prison market. A guitar-playing friend of Joe's popped in, and brought some Lebanese with him. One of the talents Joe possessed, discernably the only one, was the ability to play the guitar. He was a magician with it. That night as the effect of the dope pervaded my senses, his magic seemed particularly intensified. It was always a wonder to me, that those broken, dirty fingernails could pick those strings so unerringly; or the driving, foot-stamping responses he could invoke, when he chose to strum. Even the knowledge that he had been an occasional busker outside, only helped marginally for one to appreciate that it was indeed that unkempt ragbag, who was the author of such captivating auditory effects.

As I sat and listened that evening it gradually filtered through our parade of personal thoughts, that the grass or dope or both were producing a rare mood; it had induced in us, as cannabis occasionally does, a spirit of unreal benevolence.

It was good to be alive. Joe's filthy room seemed comfortable and lived in. It was a mood in which high security criminals as we were supposed to be; men in whom the evil weeds of revenge and retribution had found the perfect climate, could, without recourse to holy books or holy men, forgive those who had trespassed against them, and in the same spirit of simple trust, beg the forgiveness of those whom they had trespassed against.

Joe looked up suddenly and smiled, his congenitally wrinkled face grew more wrinkled, and all his blackened, broken teeth came into view, like the burnt stumps of trees in the aftermath of a forest fire.

"Good 'ere ennit?" he said. Ow can they make this gear illegal, an still sell booze in the pubs? Can you tell me that, captain?"

I could not.

"'Ow can they ban this gear, and let tobacco be sold all over the gaff? Does that make any sense to you, Captain?"

It did not.

"This is the only thing I've ever took, puff I mean, which 'as made me feel 'alf human. All the silly bits of violence I been involved in, 'as been because of drink. I'd never 'ave done them, if I'd 'a stayed on this gear. Know what I mean, Captain?"

I did.

There was nothing I could say on the subject of cannabis that Joe had not heard before. I just sat there, and nodded and wagged my head as counterpoint to his rhetoric.

"Let's go see 'ow the old bastard is gettin' on, Captain," he said. "Thin red line of empire and all that."

Of all the suggestions Joe could have made at that time, that one complemented our mood most appropriately. We felt a sense of comradely compassion for the old man who had spent most of his life in prisons; a man indiscriminately produced by the conflict between state and individual, and who appeared to have no constructive aims or purpose for a life outside; to whom prison was home, and where all his friends lived; a man who evaluated the quality of life only in terms of a comparison between the different regimes of the prisons he had lived in.

Our first impression as we stepped into his cell was that it was empty. He lay submerged under blankets, and discarded clothes on his bed, with only the white fringe of his hair showing. There was no familiar tremor; he lay stock still, like a cloth doll.

"The light ale 'as cured his shakes," Joe said.

"Do you think he's OK? I've never seen him without the shakes."

He groaned softly, and shifted his position, so that his eyes and nose came into view.

"You orright, you silly old sod?" Joe asked. There was masked concern in his intonation. He did not have to tell me that he too had, in moments of dread introspection, projected himself in later years into the institutionalized ghost that Shaky was to us. All it would take was a couple of long sentences, and that would be us lying there in that anonymous cell.

Shaky stirred again; his eyelids fluttered like dying moths.

"Mam? Is that you, mam?" he murmured.

"Don't give me that crap, you slippery old bastard," Joe said. "You know who I am. Do I look like your mum for crissake?"

To be fair to Joe he didn't look like anyone's mother that I knew of, or come to that anyone's father, that I knew of.

"Sorry, Joe," Shaky whispered. "I must a' been dreamin'. Thought I was at the seaside with me mam and dad."

"Orright, orright,' Joe said. 'You're breakin' our 'earts. We heard all that before. All we come to do is find out 'ow you're feelin'. That's all. We don't want your life story."

"I feel…oh, I feel…" Shaky said barely audible, then lapsed into total silence.

"Yeah? How do you feel?" Joe asked, as we leaned forward to hear what he had to say. We had expected to hear of some unusual symptom of acute alcoholic poisoning. Shaky made a great effort, summoning up all the pockets of breath in his body.

"I feel like a nice hot cuppa tea, and a slice of toast," he said loudly and firmly.

"Toldja he was a conniving old bastard didn' I," Joe said, belying the fact that he was quite relieved to know the old fellow was not too ill.

Joe made some tea, and I brought him half a packet of ginger biscuits from the cardboard status symbol box, under my bed. He claimed they were of a brand and substance that he was particularly attached to, and accompanied the statement with fierce slurping and chomping noises.

Having poured his tea into a blue plastic pint mug Joe offered it to him, then withheld it. "Not so fast, mister," he said. "Before you drink the tea or get your gums around the bikkis, we want a song out a'you."

"I don't know any songs," Shaky said. His trembling had resumed, and he had gone back to whispering, looking forlorn.

"Oh, yes, you bloody do," Joe said. "You kept the whole bleedin' spur up till gone two last night. You ain't gettin' any tea, till you've sung us a song."

"Them were hymns," Shaky groaned. "Religious like. You lot wouldn't like 'em."

"Whaddya mean *you* lot. You takin' the piss, you ungrateful old bastard. Did you know the captain 'ere is one of them Hairy Krishna lot? Them with the bells and big tits. He knows all about hymns and that. Used to be a priest on the out, didn'tcha, Captain?" I affirmed silently with palms pressed together.

"Go on, give the Captain a quick 'Rock of Ages', like you done last night," Joe said.

"I suppose I could do a short one. Me voice 'as lost all its strength," Shaky said.

Shaky sat up in bed, and Joe bundled some loose clothes off his bed into a pillow for his back. He sang in a determined high pitched reedy voice; Joe and I were pleased to note that he was shaking quite normally again. This is what he sang.

> Jesus bids us shine,
> With a pure clear light;
> Like a little candle,
> Burning in the night.

We applauded vigorously. Shaky objected that the clapping hurt his ears.

"That's show business, old son," Joe said. "You got to get used to things like that."

Shaky shook some tea into the general direction of his mouth, and ate a couple of biscuits. He said his gums were so hard now, that he used them like teeth, and demonstrated how tough they were, by snapping a ginger biscuit between them.

"See what I mean?" he asked. "I feels ever so much better now; I think me voice 'as come back. I could sing another song for you lads now."

And so he did; then another, and another, and another, one hymn it seems priming the next one; he gathered fervour and became unstoppable. The hot tea had reactivated the effects of the hooch.

When we left him he appeared oblivious of our departure, engrossed in losing the words from a verse of 'Onward Christian Soldiers'.

When I got back to my cell that night, it was with a vague notion that Joe was going to finish the teddies for delivery the next day. It was my own pleasantly drowsy condition that alerted me to the possibility, that if the dope was having that effect on me, my work's manager was tucked up for the night, snoring his head off.

At ten o'clock when the night sanitation facility (the chance to use running water and a flushing toilet) came into operation, I pressed the GO button on the console and went out. One of the computer-controlled features of this privilege was that only one person at any time, was allowed on to the landing, between the hours of ten and six in the morning.

As always the soundless sterility of the corridor, and general purpose area leading into the recess, had an eerie, unreal quality, that was strangely disquieting.

One knew that behind every numbered door men were living lives of determined desperation; each one fabricating a future for himself through tunnels of private fantasy; some, meeting life with humour and optimism; others in whom optimism had withered into the hair shirt of resignation. Yet there outside, it was as tranquil and orderly as an unpupiled classroom.

I crept along soundlessly, barefoot, as I had it in mind to catch the work's manager neglecting his duties, and play a practical joke on him. Moving the spyhole cover carefully, I surveyed the scene.

Joe's cell was like no other in the prison; there was junk everywhere. One corner was a tumbling confusion of assorted empty bottles and cartons. On the wall opposite his bed, what had once been a fitted blue formica cabinet had been chopped about and altered, to make a work bench for his guitar repairs; three unstrung guitars lay stacked on top of two empty budgie cages. The drawing board, the central feature in most cells; the focal point that filled out the personality, that inhabited the cell, was missing. Joe had no photographs to pin up. The board had been sliced up into three equal planks to make book shelves. Intermittently, among the science fiction paperbacks and coverless, mutilated, girlie magazines, training shoes in various stages of decay poked out.

A first time visitor to his cell would have concluded by numerical justification, that the bookshelf was in truth a shoe rack. He would have been right; this was Joe's secondhand shoe display cabinet. Each pair of shoes had a piece of string with a price tag hanging from it. The figures on the price tags were directly and proportionately related to the proprietor's financial health. When the bookies were chasing him, the shoes were marked down to a modest 5 or 10p; however, when Lady Luck smiled on him, those same shoes shot up to an astonishing and unsaleable 199p.

On the wall behind his bed he had painted a slogan, with a brush that had begun the sentence thickly larded with green paint that had dried up towards the end. The message was still appreciable. It said: MODERATION IS FOR MONKS. Supportive of that sentiment, along the wall by his bed there were two large posters; one was of Jimi Hendrix, and the other of an anguished Janis Joplin. On the floor beside his bed there was a long haired grey rug of extraordinary fertility; it was host to many species of animal and plant life. I had once, on my hands and knees aided by a magnifying glass, pursuing a small piece of dope that had slipped off our pipe, abandoned that search, in favour of studying the tiny animal and plant life that thrived in its hairy folds. Apropos of that investigation, I had suggested, that from time to time, say once a year, it should be brushed, beaten, hosed, or in some other way be made less hospitable to the life forms that infested it. I had been instantly reprimanded.

"Don'tcha know anythin' about the care and maintenance of fine carpets? 'Course, I forgot, comin' from India, you wouldn't know about things like that, wouldja? Don't 'ave carpets an' that in mud 'uts do ya? Well, let me tell you, clever bollocks, good carpets should never be brushed or beaten or hosed." He made the verbs sound gross acts of vandalism.

"Now I'm gonna tell you somethin' that may come in 'andy, if you ever get asked out to somewhere nice, where there's carpets on the floor." He shrugged and grimaced in a way that suggested I should not bank on that happening to me.

"Carpets should only ever be lightly dusted once in a while, or gently patted into shape. Anyway, a bit of ash is good for them. Brings up the natural pile, like."

I could have argued the point, pointing out that the deep pile carpet he referred to, was just an oversize hairy doormat from Woolworths; that its singed edges proclaimed a participation in at least one cell 'burn out'; further, that yes, I had heard that specious household myth about ash being good for a carpet, but how was it possible to stretch the therapeutic qualities of ash, to include droppings of egg yolk, dribblings of honey, and clots of peanut butter, to name only the encrusted smudges I could identify. I could have gone on in this fashion, but I did not. There had been a compelling reason why I had not. I was smoking his dope, and it is inadvisable in those circumstances, to criticize the cherished appurtenances of one's neighbour's house too strongly, in case he terminates his generosity.

That night, my single scanning eye traversing the room was halted by the rug, not because of any academic interest in the flora and fauna that abounded in it, but for a flagrant violation of company rules taking place on it.

Joe was sitting on a tubular prison chair by the side of the rug. On the rug a once white, now indeterminately coloured plastic bowl lay half filled with nominally soapy water, the colour and consistency of diesel oil; my work's manager was washing his feet. It was a rare moment.

Compilers of the wing gossip column were insistent, that Joe bathed four times a year. Joe was equally insistent that that was a gross exaggeration. No one had ever seen him washing any other part of his anatomy in between these special occasions. My initial desire to congratulate him turned into an emotion less charitable, when the full import of what he was doing got through to me. He had taken his right foot out of the diesel and looked at it admiringly, maternally, as though he was a mother duck with one of her favourite ducklings. He then wiped it dry by stamping on the hairy mat (towels were a needless modern affectation in Joe's life) and it was then my chairman's blood boiled; he thrust his foot into what appeared to be a cloth bag or foot warmer. It had taken me a few seconds, hampered by the restricted view through the spy hole, to realise that the cloth bag, was the half stuffed teddy.

And there he was, the picture of domestic quietude one foot in the diesel, the other snuggling into the half made teddy, sipping tea and puffing at a rollup; he exuded a sort of post-coital bliss. He had discovered that if he wiggled his toes buried in the foam by the teddy's neck, he could make its head bob up and down. I could tell by the stoned grin of amusement, that he found this spectacle rivetingly entertaining. I stood at the door and gnashed my teeth as chairman of great companies do, when they are very angry or distraught, at a mindless abuse of company products.

"Oh, yeah! Oh, yeah! I'll soon put a stop to that my filthy footed friend," I thought.

I had five minutes, stretched to seven, as my share of the night sanitation period; after that, lights would flash, and a voice veiled in jocularity, would call me back like a boat in a pleasure park: come in number 5, your time is up. I had to act quickly if I was going to disrupt my work's manager's puppeteering performance.

I waited at the door till I judged his motor coordination to be at its weakest level; a moment in which he had ceased to wiggle his toes in the teddy and was in the act of pulling his other foot out of the diesel.

He had the same rapturous look of wonderment on his face, as he watched the water dripping off his scrawny foot. If a soliloquy of his thoughts could have been heard, they would have said, "five little toes, heel, ankle, skin, bone, muscle,—well, gristle anyway, not another one like it in the whole wide world, and it's all mine, and what's more I have another one like it stashed away in the silly old company's teddy bear. Ha! Ha! Good job the stuffy old captain can't see me. Ho! Ho!

I chose that moment to hammer the door with all my strength and shout, "Oi, police, fire, guard," or words of that emotive order. The neighbourhood reacted with curses and groans. I was not unduly worried about that; it was the less prestigious part of the landing, and there would be no comebacks from the disturbance.

The effect on Joe was electric. Ideally I had hoped to topple him from his chair, but he managed to keep his balance by plonking his dripping foot heavily into the bowl, causing a fair amount of the diesel to slop over the sides.

He looked very disgruntled standing there in his underpants with one foot in the bowl. He had guessed instantly, after the initial shock, that only someone as elevated as the company chairman would have the nerve to disturb him thus. What was meant to be a truculent swagger as he came towards the door, turned into a circus clown shuffle; the teddy still fixed to his foot like a giant carpet slipper designed by Salvador Dali, flapped its arms and legs as he limped along.

"Yeah? What do you want?" he glared at me.

I made a hasty calculation of the level of his annoyance; it was at "I am going on strike" point, and the future of African George's teddy bahs was balanced precariously on it. A head-on confrontation with one's work force was out; a chatty, informal style of speech, with just a touch of acidity was called for.

"Ah! There you are my man," I said. "I hope I haven't called at an inauspicious time."

"As it 'appens you 'aven't," he said. "You're just in time to accept my resignation."

"Sorry, old chap,' I said. "I'd like to help but you know company regulations as well as I do: resignations have to be tendered in broad daylight. And incidentally, while we are on the subject of company regulations would you mind getting your foot out of the company product's face."

"Fuck the company," he shouted. He goose-stepped around the

cell, stamping the teddy down forcefully on each stride; bits of foam flew out like frightened insects.

"I see. Reverting to character are we?"

"Yeah. Yeah!" he chanted, as he stomped around the room, giving an occasional Hitler salute.

In a voice softly reproachful, I asked if he had considered African George and his babas?

"Fuck African George and his babas," he said, and continued to stomp around the cell.

"So this is British craftsmanship?"

He stopped his marching and came up to the spyhole.

"No, that ain't British craftsmanship. I'll show you what British craftsmen do when they got the 'ump."

He took the teddy bear off his foot. For a moment I thought he was going to jump on it. I wished he had. His underpants fell to the floor and there he was in a post bowel-movement posture, using the company product as toilet paper; more bits of foam flew out like frightened insects.

My partial view of the proceedings through the spy hole, visually sensitized by the cannabis, gave me the illusion that a company teddy bear had come rampantly to life, and was earnestly and at high speed, sodomizing the work's manager. There was it seemed a future for a sex toy line in teddy bears after all.

The chairman's patience was exhausted.

"I am pleased to see you have washed your feet," I said. "I shall be coming for you first thing in the morning with the big blunt saw out of the hobby room. You know, the rusty one that looks like your teeth. I am going to remove your legs at the knee, and give them to African George in lieu of the teddies. He's often mentioned to me, man to man, that he would like a bit of Tandoori Englishman for his breakfast."

"On your bike," Joe said. "You 'aven't read your United Nations statistics lately 'ave you? One Englishman is worth twenty six Indians."

I was of course alarmed to hear of this equation.

"How many?"

"Well, at least ten anyway."

"Thank God for that," I said. "You had me worried there for a minute. Anyway, you can expect to see me in the morning without the other nine. And by the way, you can safely dispose off your shoes, and let your socks walk away; you won't be needing anything like that after tomorrow."

He was still yelling and stamping around as I closed the door to my cell at the quiet end of the landing. My dreams that night should have been of a vengeful African George, chasing me round the football field, clutching an assegai of formidable sharpness in his chubby fist, ripping off tremendous Maggie Thatchahs at every stride; the fact that they did not, was because I knew that whereas I was now fair game for a practical joke, my work's manager would not let the company down. I lay in bed the next morning, awake, sentient, but not altogether in gear, the familiar early morning sounds of running water, and snatches of veiled accusations as to who had the Sunday People, ebbed in and out of my consciousness. The prisoners who worked in the shops were locking their doors, getting ready to go to work; a period of unfailing gloating satisfaction for me, knowing I could stay in bed for another whole torporous hour.

My door suddenly became the mute recipient of a powerful bombardment; in the cacophony, I could identify the work's manager's lewd tones, a metal prison tray being used as a battering instrument, and heavy-duty work boots. The door handle moved, but the door would not open; I had my chock-shaped wedge under the door, and no one, tea carrying friend, or battery-in-sock bearing foe, could get in without my cooperation.

By the time I had pulled the wedge out and opened the door, Joe had got rid of the steel tray, and was standing in the doorway with his arms full of teddy bears, and a jug of tea. He had the look of a malicious gargoyle; that is to say he looked quite normal.

"Ah! There you are, my man," he said in a passable imitation of my inflexion. "I hope I haven't called at an awkward time?" Then reverting to his own style of speech, he said, "Thought I'd let the firm down there, didn't cha?"

I admitted that I had been worried.

"Thin red line of empire, mate," he said, in the act of putting the two teddies on my pillow.

"More like, thick brown line of empire, you dirty bastard," I said, and with that utterance, realised how close my pillow was to being contaminated. I lunged forward to defend my territorial rights. He, insisting that it was part of company tradition to place finished articles on the chairman's pillow, danced around the cell, using the teddies one in each hand like boxing gloves, trying to land them on my face. He was chanting to the rhythm of his footwork: 'knick knack lights are flashin'; we are goin' Paki bashin'.'"

An aroma of cheap talcum powder pervaded the room as the teddies bounced off my outstretched protective arms; and it was the conjecture as to what other smells the talcum powder was keeping at bay, that impelled me to defend myself so competently. I ducked, and weaved, and blocked, as chairmen of great corporations are trained to do.

After a few minutes he was exhausted, and flopped into my chair; I was able to lift the teddies from him by their ears and put them by the door.

"We'll 'ave to 'ave a board meetin' tonight, to get company rules sorted out," he gasped. "I always thought I 'ad to leave finished goods on the chairman's bed. Now you've gone an' changed the rules. I demand an enquiry."

"Bollocks," I said.

There are times when the muscular language of the shop floor is needed, to best notify the workers what the view from the top is like. At the board meeting that night, the chairman and the work's manager hammered out an equitable agreement after forceful debate, during which the customary illegal substance and copious quantities of tea had been drunk. It was agreed as follows: the chairman was not to disrupt the work's manager's ruminative ablutions during the hours of darkness, and the work's manager was pledged by sacred company oath not to (a) wear the company products on his feet and (b) ever allow the said company products to come into contact with even more disagreeable parts of his body.

On receipt of the teddies, African George banged them together like cymbals and a delicate veil of talcum powder hung between us.

"Mmmmm, nice, mmmmm smell," he said; there was the slightest note of enquiry.

"Just a small company frill, excellency," I said hastily.

"We lightly sprinkle holy scented ash, from the wholly filthy Ganges, on the goods of esteemed customers. There is no extra charge."

We exchanged friendly Maggie Thatchahs, and he asked to be remembered to the work's manager, with a special message that he, African George, would be pleased to be a referee to the high quality of Joe's workmanship.

After this contract the output of our company plummeted. We were lucky to sell one teddy a week; not enough to affect our debts decisively.

It was in this stagnant period of company history that Australian Barry, brash, cocky, and confident, came to me with a proposition.

Chapter 16

What he had to propose was, as I expected, illegal.

"You don't have to do anything. Just sit and wait for the box to arrive. Then go and sign for it, and bring it back here. That's all there is to it. In the worst way, if it all comes on top, it's got nothing to do with you. Anybody could send you anything from outside. You can't be held responsible for that. See what I mean?"

I saw clearly; in fact I was nodding my head energetically in agreement during, and after, the scheme had been outlined. It was simple enough. It was, that a friend of his would send a large box of foam rubber pieces addressed to me at the Lazy L. This would cause no security ripples, as I was a registered soft toy hobbyist, and had received other boxes sent in to me in the past.

This box would be different; secreted in a few of the thousands of pieces of foam would be pea-sized nuggets of cannabis. For the privilege of using my, as yet unblemished good name, I was to receive one third of the contraband.

My only misgiving about the venture centred around Barry's seeming inability to maintain silence. When he was involved in anything that was clandestine, the coterie that attended him also had to know about it, even if they were not actually involved in the action. But the prospect of wiping out my debts in one easy transaction, and painlessly to move into a position of creditworthiness; to have a cardboard box filled with our small symbols of status under my bed; to be able once more to invite friends in for a cup of tea knowing I also had coffee or Ovaltine; such grandiose dreams were powerful persuaders. Even in prison a branch of the Jones family is alive and well.

As something to say, for my mind was already sold on the idea, I mentioned the necessity for covertness in such an operation. He laughed derisively, for effect.

"Look at me, sport," he said. Ten years I've been inside, came in when I was twenty six, and now I'm thirty six. A decade of Christmases I've been having these bastards over. The only times I been nicked were for escaping and riots, never for drugs. Too smart for these wallies.

See? How many specials* have you known me to have? Did you ever see them find anything? No. That's because I keep my lip buttoned. There's no need for anyone except you, me, and my pal outside to know what's going on."

"What happens," I asked, "if they find the gear, let me collect it, then bust me with my hot trembling fingers deep in the gunga."

Barry shook his head sharply.

"That's not how these people work," he said.

"If they find the gear, you will never get to hear about it. You won't even be told there's a box for you, but from that time they'll be watching anything that comes in for you. That's all. Anyways there's always risk in anything we do in here. You get nothing for nothing. Anyways, faint heart never fucked fair lady."

And he smiled then, and in that slow reckless formation, I saw the ghosts of Flynn and Coleman, and Bogart; boyhood heroes who were still powerful gods to a middle-aged man not yet full grown.

So I said, "And what's more, a bird in the hand will shit on your wrist."

With those adaptable aphorisms, the criminal contract was sealed. We crossed hearts and hoped to die as quality criminals do, if we breathed a word to anyone else, and parted.

That weekend Barry had a visit, and the plan was put into operation. Neither my memory, nor reference to intermittent diary notes, are able to tell me how long we waited. The diary for those days has a single entry of greater significance. It says: Daisy wants a divorce.

---

* Special: an exercise in which a prisoner's cell is searched individually and more thoroughly than normal 'turn-over' in which the whole landing is searched.

Chapter 17

Peter Quinn had called me into his office. As though in deference to the news he was about to convey, but in truth because he was fresh from a Governor's meeting, he wore a too-tight dark suit. He wrenched his tie off, and invited me to sit down. His manner thus far had not betrayed the size or quality of the disclosure he was about to make; but when he turned after hanging up his tie on the hatstand, his guileless earthbound face was serious.

My immediate thought was that the foam rubber scam had been discovered.

"I've just been talking to Daisy," he said, glancing at the telephone. "I am afraid it's as you feared."

"As I feared, what?"

I had so many fears of various strengths; classic prisoner's nightmare scenarios, concerning a home and family that he could not see, but was a part of, and of whose deterioration he would be advised of one day without warning—as I was being advised now.

A glimmer of recognition as to what type of scenario this was, may have showed in my eyes.

He nodded. "Yes, she wants a divorce. You said you'd rather know one way or the other, didn't you? Well, I've had a long talk with her, and all her recent actions, you know, not seeing the probation officer, not writing, etc have been geared towards this. I'm sorry."

After a pause I said, "So am I, I suppose." Peter got up, and looked morosely out of the window; the sound of a cricket ball being hit followed by a shout and a laugh filtered through. A group of small birds flew in and out of the razor wire on an adjacent building.

"If you want it," Peter said, turning back, "I'll get a phone call arranged, so you can talk to her. Or arrange accumulated visits somewhere a bit closer. The Island, or Winchester, somewhere like that. This is up to you. You'll have to let me know, if you want that."

I rejected the offer instantly, instinctively. I felt no pain, or anger at the news. Just a fatalistic acceptance that whatever would be, would be; but later in the days and especially the nights when measured thoughts had their moment, I was still of that initial state of mind. It was as if objectivity had drawn a parallel between my marriage and the lingering wasting disease of a friend; when the end comes, there can only be a feeling of thankfulness, that it is all over. Now, all that remained was to ensure that the physical remains were buried with decency, but quickly.

Why then did I feel drained of strength and volition at times when I came across the memory of that single sentence? It did not seem enough: Daisy wants a divorce. I wanted more of a fuss, more histrionics and beating of breasts, and shedding of tears to end twenty years of marriage. I wanted to feel bitter, and wronged, and could not. The strongest emotion was the salt taste of sarcasm; that of the hundred years my wife had promised to wait for me, she managed four and a half.

From the beginning of our marriage, harnessed as it was in exogamy, there had been an element of dramatic symbolism, which had impelled me into the wings, to oversee our performance on stage. Even at those times when I felt we were most closely united, some component within me stood aside, to observe how the drama was unfolding; to comprehend, and direct the next act of what we were jointly creating.

And we created in those tumultuous early days of living and loving, four children. It was as their names and faces impinged on my thoughts, that hurtful twinges like mental neuralgia, provoked a moral responsibility that moved and came to life like an animal out of hibernation. In my reveries and pastiches of remembered moments, the children had stood so submissively in the shade of Daisy's personality, that I saw them as a single unit: Daisy, and the children.

On visits, (I had not seen them for nearly two years)we followed the custom of approaching each other through her; a pentangular relationship had evolved through the strictures and conditions of prison visits, of which Daisy had become the pivotal, indispensable, central part; but the distance between the points of the pentagon was increasing daily. Soon the tenuous contact maintained through letters, becoming ever more banal, and superficial, would be broken altogether. Now that the central support, and censor in the flow of emotional traffic was to be permanently removed from my life, I had the presentiment that divorce from one person could mean estrangement from four others. That was the sombre view from my prison cell; it was a hopeless empty feeling.

The fact remained that there were four human beings to whom I was father, who thought of me as such, and with whom I had lost touch. Those fast years of teenage growing up of which I had not been a part, had made strangers of them.

The urge to walk away from all my attachments, like a childish vandal unable to face what he has done; to go somewhere where no one knew me, to start afresh and pretend that I had not already lived half a life previously elsewhere, held a short reign in my mind. Its brevity was due to a simple appreciation, that if ever I did that, their shadows would haunt me, to negate any measure of pleasure, or peace, I hoped to find when these prison days were ended. In any way that was open to me, I would have to come to terms with them.

There was another insistent magnet force that held me. It was the spiritual bond, born in biology that gives the proof to the power of the units of heredity. The wizardry of genetics had cast its spell, and held me in wonderment; to look at them was to face parts of myself; I saw an element of myself in the way my daughters smiled, or the way my sons stood or walked; to recognize the light in their eyes, and to know that they shared a heritage with me, that began in a land they had never seen. They were a part of me as my wife had never been. Channels of blood and genes united us; a part of all that they were, was me. And what biology had begun my spirit acclaimed. Disused words from a semantic neighbourhood that I thought I would never visit again, words like clan and kinship, tribe and totem, sprang into my head and resonated there. I knew with certainty that I could no more walk away from them than I could from myself. They were parts of me, and I was part of them.

The emptiness I had felt was encompassed in a contour of pain that I could now define, and it deepened, for I had ceased to know how these parts worked any more. I felt the frustration of a man with a wasted limb, looking at it, knowing it was part of him, and yet not knowing how to make it respond fit into a pattern of interactive compatibility. Implicit love and affection for them had never left me, but it had been of that variety tinged by parental vigilance, which seeks to immunize, and cocoon the objects of its attention from the realities of adult life.

As I mulled over my feelings for them pensively subjective, as daybreak illuminates the sleeping hazards of an unfamiliar landscape, I perceived the fundamental handicap; the generic term 'children', hopelessly obsolete except in my own mind, had knotted them together. The threads of their individuality were lost to me. Letters were the most useless tools with which to unpick that knot. I needed to see them, to talk to them to find out what made them laugh and cry, to get to know them. And I did not know how to begin that process without Daisy.

So I foresaw with anxiety the time I would be leaving the prison to meet four enquiring young adults, strangers, to say, "How do you do,

I'm your father, remember me?" That much I knew I had to attempt; what I did not know, could not conceptualise in any way that made me feel comfortable, was the first meeting. I was nervous of it; it hung on the horizon of my thoughts during the day, and intruded into those periods of sweeping subliminal perception before I fell asleep at night, or before I was fully awake in the morning. It occurred to me, that one reason why my imagination to project myself into those first meetings had failed was because I could not envisage the physical surroundings either.

By the time the divorce was legalized I would not have a home to go to. When I did have one, I had no idea what it would look like, nor where it would be situated. It was essential underpinning, if I was to present myself as the separate independant part of their parentage. My complementary role as guardian had been removed, indeed, although I was unaware of it at the time my place had already been taken by a surrogate; my side of the double bed was no longer empty; had not been so for nearly a year.

When the issue of property settlement was pertinent, I would ensure that they continued to live in the house and home in which they had grown up. My task would be to establish my own home and presence in it somewhere, and fashion a relationship with them in which I would be a person they could respect and turn to, as a source of experience and wisdom.

There remained one other imponderable which hopefully was being pondered upon even as I conjectured, by a panel of righteous people who were empowered to set me free, or keep me in captivity: I was waiting for the decision on my third application for parole. All the officials at the lazy L who were in a position to influence that decision had given me the thumbs up, they said. Taff, who was an officer personally involved in preparing reports about me went so far as to have a bet of a Mars bar with me, that I would get it. It was a bet I fervently hoped I would lose.

Coda

In fact, I did not get parole that time, nor any other; worse, I was to lose several months remission, and not get a day back; in all I was to actually serve seven years and two months of a ten year sentence. When I met them for the first time, the children I had left behind had majored into driving licence holders, who spoke easily of bank accounts and mortgages.

My rehearsed intention to offer myself as a mature source of wisdom never got off the ground. Solemn pretensions of orthodox pater-

138

nity were blown away. And I have never been more thankful for a failure; for what grew from that misjudged attempt was a relationship towards which my personality is by nature more inclined; one in which my position is more privileged, and does not depend for its sustenance on channels of blood and genes: we became friends.

Chapter 18

When friends meet an ex-prisoner the invariable first question after the back-slapping and other expressions of welcome have been concluded is, "What was it like?" The most enlightening way to answer it is to describe a prison incident.

It may not be the whole truth about prison nor the way it affected one but it is certainly one flavour in the whole dish.

*

The sounds coming from the boiler room were not as they should have been for that time of the morning; contentious tones protested. As I got closer, one voice rose above the others. Hungarian Pete, so called because he came from Yugoslavia, was making his personality and ideolect felt.

He was shouting, "Vy am I vork in a factory, coming back 'ere. Vy is a no fuckinny hot voter. Is this a funny farmyard or a nick? Soon there be more transfer than a Kevin Keegan."

All that in conventional language was "I am not prepared to work in the prison shops, if on my return to the wing, there is no fucking hot water. Is this a mental institution or a prison? If this state of affairs persists, I am going to ask for a move to another wing."

The reference to Kevin Keegan was too oblique for me, and was probably gratuitous. Pete never wanted to be seen to be at a loss for words, even if they were not in context or comprehensible.

A screw, distinguished by his large pink ears, was trying unavailingly to shout louder than Hungarian Pete. "If you'll just belt up and look for the bloody thing, it'd be a help. It can't be far."

While the two were glaring at each other I asked onlookers what the problem was.

It appeared that the new tea boiler which had been installed had not been fully plumbed in; it was functional only with the aid of a piece of green plastic tubing which linked the main water supply to the boiler. Now, this vital piece of technology had disappeared. Result; no fuckinny hot voter.

"Well, well, and my my," I mused, as I made my way to the shower room. Such activity before lunch in a sleepy high security prison.

In the shower room I witnessed another problem. A clutch of guys were watching intently over the shoulder-high wooden doors that separated the showers from the bath. And it was in the solitary bath that the action was taking place. Harry, called Dirty Harry by personal request, the Hells Angel, was presiding. He was a big guy over six foot tall, with a huge but muscular beer gut, a prominent squint, no upper teeth, fat purple lips, and blackish hair, which seemed to have found the ideal soil; it grew everywhere, down his back, from his ears, out of his nostrils; an erratically tailored bush of it adorned his face. If one could imagine the classical concept of a concert pianist, this man was on the opposite side of that spectrum.

He was doing twelve years for taking part in an inter denominational debate, during which such pieces of cutlery as double bladed swords, axes, and machetes had been freely used; two men had been killed. Tenets of his faith were printed by word and picture all over his visible body. On his right breast he had printed in poor calligraphy, 'Wanna Fuck?' On the other breast, 'Fuck 'The Old Bill'. The rest of the messages were modifications on those two themes, except one. It was by far the most professional and conspicuous of his tribal marks; he carried it on his left forearm. It read 'Ride to live, live to ride', and was tattooed over the image of a grimacing skull. As an incidental novelty, a green bodied, black tongued snake was squirming through one of the eye sockets.

It was this arm that held the attention of the onlookers. He up held in his fingers at eye level, a dangling length of green plastic tubing; exactly such a piece as was required to solve the problem in the other place. The uncharitable among us, that is to say all of us watching, knew that it was indeed the tubing from the boiler. A makeshift funnel made from the back of a tissue box was inserted into the tubing; down that funnel Dirty Harry was pouring soapy water. A delicate beige tongue, out of keeping in so gross a face was hesitantly poised between his rubbery lips, as a directional aid to the precise task on hand. The other end of the tube had a hollow Biro stuck into it. The end of the Biro could not be seen, as it was embedded in between the buttocks of a foetally reclining, naked figure in the bath. This figure despite its uncomfortable position and unenviable predicament at the sharp end of a pen, was nevertheless explaining the circumstances quite lucidly.

"Bastard," he said, "two gs of pure Chang in a charger stuck up my bum. If it gets out, I'm brown bread. Brown bread—dead," he added, grinning cheerfully.

All that in conventional language was; "This is an unfortunate state of affairs. I have two grams of heroin originating from the

Chiang Mai province of Thailand in a specially made phial, stuck in my anus. If the phial leaks, I am dead."

The recumbent form was Dirty Harry's best buddy Slippery, so called and not by personal request, because of his adroitness at defrauding people in drugs deals. He was the number one drug afficianado at the Lazy L, with aspirations to the All England title. He had used, continued to use whenever he could, any sort of illegal drug that came his way without discrimination.

His bone-thin frame exhibited in parts the savagery with which he had abused his body. In the area of his upper arms, at the place where biceps should normally sprout, there was just hacked-about mutilated flesh, that hung in lumps and tatters like the bark of a young tree vandalized by children. "Five years of Physeptone shots done that," he would say, reverentially stroking his scars with a touch that one might reserve for the extravagant, yet fondly remembered memorabilia of one's youth. Sometimes when Slippery was talking to someone and the conversation bored him, he would switch off; he would close his eyes and drift away into a trance-like state, while gently nodding his head in seeming acquiescence to the speaker. The rest of his body see-sawed imperceptibly heel to toe, heel to toe. Suddenly he would come out of it, attracted back to reality by some key word or phrase that was important to his existence.

"What? What was that again?" he would ask. "I must have missed a bit there. I was projecting then, see? I can do it any time. Astral projecting. Just like a bird, straight out of the nick. Zoom:"

One such word was drug. It thrilled him like no other in the language; when the adjective 'illegal' qualified the substance, it became irresistible. He had to try it; the effect it would have on him was of secondary importance. He believed he said, that there was a psychic experience called the ultimate high; in dedicated pursuit of which he was willing to try any pill, powder, mushroom or medicine: the perpetual alchemist in search of the transmuting agent. His personality had been made definitive for us by an earlier incident.

A new arrival at the Lazy L, clearing out the bits and pieces left behind by the previous occupant of his cell, had found two capsules wrapped in brown paper taped to the underside of his chair. The careful, clandestine manner in which it had been placed there, suggested a marketable value; so the new guy made enquiries as to the appropriate authority he would take them to for analysis. The answer was unanimous; Slippery knew more about pills and capsules than the encyclopedia.

142

A few of us, academic observers, went along with the new guy to hear Slippery's pronouncement.

"What do you make of these," the new guy had asked, offering the capsules to Slippery. They were plastic-coated, and had the colouration of a wasp, yellow and black; the sort of pills one felt instinctively that belonged in the poison section of a chemists shop.

"Well, well, what have we here," Slippery said. The light of scientific curiosity gleamed in his eye. He weighed them in his hand, sniffed them, held them to his ear and shook them, looked at them against the light, and then as though these methods had proved unsatisfactory, he swallowed them. We stood looking at him for a few seconds, not comprehending that that was the end of his investigation. We thought, that as is the custom of professional people such as wine tasters, it was an analytic skill he was demonstrating, and that he would regurgitate the pills at any moment, to say, "Ah yes, I know what these are, and then go on to name the year of their manufacture, and the pharmacy of their origin. But no; that was the end of the show.

"If you lads want to come back in a couple of hours, I'll tell you what they were," he had said, smiling, with his gentle soft focus eyes.

"Christ!" the new guy said, "What a geezer! Thanks for bringing me along to meet him. Its nice to know there's some sensible people in this nick!"

When we checked with Slippery two hours later, he was vague. "Pills? What pills? I never had any pills off you blokes."

"Oh, yes, you did," we chorused, "standing right there in front of your pad."

"Come to think of it, I seem to remember that now," he said. "Big, flat, white jobs, were they?"

"They were long yellow and black jobs," we corrected.

"Yah, yeah, it's all comin' back to me now. You blokes asked me what they were and I said I didn't know, and then you all went away..."

"Wrong," we said. "You swallowed them."

"Did I really! Well now, there's a thing: Was I in the fifth dimension when I done that?" he asked earnestly.

"That's hard to say," we said. "We have never been there."

He then confounded us with the weight of his knowledge in other worldly matters; he allowed us to view the unreal architecture of his mind. We had come away curiously satisfied with his non-explanation. We never found out what the pills were.

Slippery and Dirty Harry were bonded in a simple symbiotic

relationship, Slippery foraged for drugs for their mutual consumption; Harry provided the muscle to keep people from thumping Slippery.

The onlookers at the drama in the bath were multinational, as befits a prison in ex-colonial Britain. There was Australian Barry, hairpin-bent in laughter, in one corner of the bathroom, the American Chuck seemed to have the role of Technical Adviser. The Sheikh representing Asia was leaning on the door, twirling his flyaway moustaches and chuckling.

I could not quite see the action over their heads, so I got a steam-sodden chair and stood on it.

That displeased Dirty Harry.

"Christ! Is there any more of youse out there wants to come and watch. Like a bleedin' United Nations meeting it's turned out."

As though in support of that simile Hungarian Pete walked in making searching, unfulfilled noises. He saw what was happening, and a look of hurt shock spread over his face.

"Vy is a hot voter pipe stuck up in his bum?" he asked. Dirty Harry didn't answer. He just squinted at him so horribly, so malevolently, that Pete retreated as if struck, climbed on to my chair and tried to edge me off.

"Do you mind," I said forcefully. "Get your own seat; it's people like you, start wars, infringing on territorial rights." Pete seemed to have forgotten his search for the pipe; he was smiling broadly.

"You have your name writing on this chair, vanka? You vont a trouble mith Yugoslavia? Vot you fighting mith, chappati bombs?"

The cold war of words over the rights to the chair devolved into a warm one; Pete was trying to board it, I was trying to repel the invader. As is customary in such disputes, the territory itself was the chief sufferer; the chair was in danger of being torn in two.

"For fuck's sake," Dirty Harry bellowed. In the small room his voice had the tonal resonance of a bullfrog going into battle. Hungarian Pete and I fell silent. There was a greater issue at stake; but issue, or lack of it, was precisely what was raising Dirty Harry's blood pressure.

"What do I do now?" he asked Chuck. You were the one told us to try it. Now the bleedin' water won't go down."

"I told you before you started," Chuck began patiently, "to get all the loops and squirls outa' the toobing. You wouldn't listen. How do you think the water is going to get past all those knots. You English guys do any elementary physics in school?"

Harry looked confused trying to remember what school was.

"Physics, man! Think physics!" Chuck urged. Harry was squinting wildly at the cardboard funnel which was beginning to disintegrate with the weight of water in it.

The words physics and school acted like the tines of an accurate fork on my memory, to pick out a morsel of knowledge that I felt was pertinent in this situation.

"Water does not go uphill against the force of gravity," I shouted, authoritatively above the sound of Barry's laughter.

"I am an agree mith that," Hungarian Pete said.

Dirty Harry directed an utterly contemptuous squint towards me.

"No one's tryin' to get water *up hill*, son, we're tryin' to get it up his *arse*, got that? Comprendy?"

He appealed to the front row of his audience. "Hark at them two, Khruschev and Gandy. First they was arguin' over who should have the chair now they want to be comedians as well."

The Sheikh raised his hand to stop the cross talk. He spoke quietly.

"As you chaps know, I am a graduate of the University of California. I feel therefore that I am qualified to dispense a few words of advice in this crisis."

"At least a bloke who wants to help," Harry said. "What do you reckon then?"

The Sheikh was about to answer but Chuck interrupted him.

"Pardon me, sir," he said addressing the Sheikh, "could you tell the rest of us dumbos what faculty you were associated with at UCLA? If I am to be dismissed from my office as scientific adviser, I demand to know the credentials of my successor."

We voiced our support for his request.

"Ignore these people from rent-a-crowd, my friend," the Sheikh said. "I have the answer to this problem. In fact it is quite fundamental." He dug Chuck in the ribs.

"Get that? *Fundamental*?"

One of the lesser pastimes of the Sheikh and Chuck was pun making. They were usually of a quality that flew right over Dirty Harry's head.

"What's that?" he asked, warily.

"What you want is a pump," the Sheikh said.

"Vot he vont is a Dyno Rod job," Hungarian Pete shouted.

"I am an agree mith that," I shouted too.

Hungarian Pete riffled over with satisfaction. Usually his comments in any group discussion were regarded as irrelevant.

"Something like a bicycle pump," the Sheikh thought out aloud, "would do the trick."

"Naw, you'd never find anything like that in this nick," Dirty Harry said. He portrayed by the affected weariness of his expression that he had finally accepted that the Home Office would never provide such basic facilities as bicycle pumps for prisoners.

"On the other hand," the Sheikh said, "the human lungs can be adapted in an emergency as a machine for air propulsion. Do you get my meaning, my friend? Or should I draw you some simple diagrams."

The funnel which had been steadily collapsing fell to the floor like an over ripe fruit. Harry stamped on it with feeling.

"That's it. That's the last time we use duff Yankee gear," he said.

"Just like their bikes, fall to bits at the first sign of a rough ride."

One eye was fixed steadily on Chuck, while the other by the special configuration of his eyeballs, seemed to be looking at the trod-on and kicked-at remains of the funnel. He interspersed his comments with a medley of jeering barks.

"We don't need any more cheap American garbage," the Sheikh said.

"Now attend to my words, my man, and we shall snatch victory from wherever victories are normally snatched from." Dirty Harry looked at the Sheikh favourably.

"Go on, doctor," he said, "you're in charge now. I've just sacked the Yank. What's the next move."

"The whole exercise is fairly simple," the Sheikh said. "Just get a few inches of water in that tube, and then borrowing from the phraseology of Shakespeare imitate the action of the whale, and borrowing from the phraseology of more recent poets, blow it up Slippery's Khyber Pass."

Chuck interrupted, "Don't you think you owe it to your client to tell him about the possibility of a blowback? Got it, *blowback*."

"By 'Jove! Yes of course," the Sheikh said. "For a moment I didn't recognize the vulgar Americanism. We medical chaps call it praecipitum ejaculari. Latin, in case you don't know. Anyway, coming back to the problem; my client is not stupid, as one look at the literature on his body must tell you. When the crucial moment is imminent, he will hop nimbly out of the way, and hopefully, anything or things that come hurtling out will hit that dirty Australian convict bastard right in the eye. That should stop him laughing and make him take life seriously."

The dirty Australian convict bastard continued to be swamped by laughter, which was giving him a stitch he said.

At the mention of blowback a haze of indecision settled on Dirty

146

Harry's face. His movements of bustling assurance under the Sheikh's direction had slowed to a shuffle; his ferociously crossed eyes looked uneasy. The term blowback had conjured up eventualities his simple brigand's mind had not taken into consideration. But he exhibited the universal maxim that even the simplest soul hides somewhere a concealed element of self preservation. He waggled the tube a few times inconsequentially and turned to Chuck.

"H'ya're then," he said. "I'll hold the gubbins, while you give it your best shot, good buddy."

He squinted winningly at Chuck, and laughed a carefree comradely laugh, loaded with insincerity. Chuck's reaction was immediate and definite.

"Who? Who, *me*? Are you kiddin? You just fired me, remember? No surr, no way. You took this smart talkin Pakistani khan man," he nudged the Sheikh, "*khan* man on to your payroll, and put me out in the cold. Sides, I'm a Pentecostal, Buddhistic, Non Conformist gentle sort of person. My religion would not allow..."

"Yeah, yeah," Dirty Harry sneered; a visual assault of cracked, purple, salami lips over the blank where incisors should have been.

"We know all about you Yanks, we seen you performin' in Vietnam. Bloody shambles."

"Yanks never blow up a banjo with a cow's arse, in Vietnam," Hungarian Pete shouted.

The Sheikh turned around to point out that Pete had got the idiom askew.

"Never mind, I am an agree mith that," I said.

Hungarian Pete beamed at me, and Dirty Harry in his anti American mood, beamed at both of us.

He tentatively offered the tube to the Sheikh.

"My friend," the Sheikh said gravely. "I would be pleased to help you, but alas, Islam also specifically forbids such activities. But please be assured that morally I am one hundred per cent with you. Why not try one of the gentlemen standing on the chair? They have contributed nothing practical to these proceedings."

Dirty Harry's eyes, each one in its turn, raked over Hungarian Pete and me, we each in our turn, in our own way, declined the invitation.

"Fuck this," Dirty Harry said, "it's doin' me head in."

"Next time you tribes from Europe and Asia get your arsholes in trouble don't look to the US cavalry to help you out," Chuck said. "I'm writing to the President tonight to cancel all our treaties with you guys."

"What about me, sport?" Barry asked. "I'm not with these guys."

"You're fine at the moment Aussie," Chuck said. "I'll advise the President to leave ANZUS in force. But watch your step. When Uncle Sam gets mad, WOW, he gets real mad."

"Who is a Anne's arse?" Hungarian Pete asked me in an undertone.

"Never mind about that," I whispered. "Just watch the fat dirty man. He's going to do something very clever now. Watch carefully."

Dirty Harry had been emitting an assortment of throat clearing noises.

"Just gettin' me breath together," he explained.

"I ain't scared of any fucking blowback. Blowback: Huh! What's that? I'll give the bastard blowback. There ain't nothin' born can blow Big Harry back."

"Huff and a puff and a phoo!" he practised a trio of long expulsions on Chuck and the Sheikh. They winced three times in response, as they got the full flavour of it. Having backed away from Dirty Harry's breath on many previous occasions, even in spacious corridors, I was able to sympathise.

"By God!" the Sheikh said fervently, "I think we have the right man for the job."

Then Dirty Harry puffed himself up, looked at the assembled crowd with the challenging air of a circus strongman, and pursed his lips to form two hairy balls; he looked all set to blow Slippery clean into the fifth dimension.

At this point Slippery said, "Jesus, what *am* I thinking of," and leapt out of the bath. The tubing followed him for a few paces like the life cord of an astronaut in space before falling away.

"Well, I never! Fancy that! Shit and corruption," and other expressions of wonderment suggested to us that he was a man stunned by a compelling revelation. He pulled on his pants hurriedly, and hurriedly left the room. In his haste he nearly knocked down a frail elderly man in an equal rush to get into the room.

The newcomer was the geriatric delinquent Scot, known to us as Shaky or 'the old bastard', cotton-thatched gnome-sized, and agile as a performing monkey. He had been posted outside as lookout and it was this function he came in to fulfil.

"Screw comin, screw comin," he repeated in an approximation of an articulate robot. With that he whipped out half a towel from a voluminous kangaroo pouch pocket of his overalls and started to rub energetically at a non existent mark on the tiles.

The screw he was warning us of was hard on his shoulder. It was large pink ears, last seen scratching his head in the boiler room.

"Why don't cha shout that a bit louder so's the whole nick can hear you, you silly old bugger," he said "What are you blokes up to in 'ere anyway?"

He advanced into the room to find out what was causing the crush in the bath house, when he did a double take and went back to where Shaky was polishing the tiles.

"Where did you get that towel from?" he demanded. "That's a staff towel you got there."

"Staff towel? How d'you make that out guvnor?" Shaky asked, in a tone marinated in hurt innocence.

"You know very well what I mean. That's the third one gone missing this week. Don't tell me you didn't know the difference. Ours don't have a blue border. Anyway they are more fluffier." He paused to consider whether English grammar was safe with him.

The rest of the room came to life like a video cassette started in the middle, with contrived half sentences, and actions to match. Hungarian Pete and I had jumped off the chair at the first sign of the screw, but not quickly enough for him not to have registered it. He didn't try to hide his puzzlement as we passed.

I was saying to Pete, "...While the constituents are prepositional, adjectival, and nominal, but of course the construction is adverbial. Do you see what I mean?"

Pete didn't have too much to say to that, just kept nodding his head as we passed the screw and old Shaky who were engaged in a tug of war with the towel.

Outside Hungarian Pete drew me aside confidentially. "Who is a Anne's arse?" he asked. "They two is always try to put a wool in my eyes."

Hungarian Pete had never forgiven Chuck and the Sheikh for a joke they had played on him when he was new at the Lazy L. They had conned him into believing that what he wore for reading were his testicles; had shown unnatural goodwill in helping him write a composition for the English remedial class, taken by a humourless matronly lady who had for Pete the unusual attraction of having been to Belgrade for her last summer holidays. Pete had got it into his head that she was the key to parole; a person who would speak up for the courteous, misunderstood, foreign gentleman. It was an idea he had projected meticulously.

The composition was entitled 'One day in my life'. Chuck suggested the story line and The Sheikh supplied the opening sentence.

"You see my friend," The Sheik had said, "the first line of any treatise or in this case corpus I should say, should hold the attention of the reader. If you wish to impress this lady, as I believe you do, please leave the matter with me. I am a man of great circumspection in affairs of the heart. I can guarantee that she will remember the opening sentence for a long time to come."

After The Sheikh and Chuck had polished it, picked at it, and shrieked over it, this is how one day in the life of Hungarian Pete began.

"When I am a voke up udder morning, my testicles vos gone. I am a think someone has stole them avay." The rest of the two-page essay was a narrative of his attempts to reclaim the runaway parts of his anatomy. Chuck and the Sheik used all the sit-com ambiguities to develop the double entendre. It ended with a reference to the soft yellow cloth he used to keep them clean. "When I am a go to bed, I am a polish my testicles shiny bright for a next morning."

There was no way of knowing what impact it had on the teacher, and we were left wondering whether we were right in thinking that she had no sense of humour, or if it was of a category too poker-faced for our appreciation.

She had underlined the word wherever it occurred, and given the Sheik's enthusiasm, it made the pages look as though they had suffered the torture of a thousand cuts. At the end in the same punitive colour she had added these comments.

> You must use the dictionary to check the meaning of similar sounding words in English.
>
> Spelling—still poor.
> Vocabulary—getting better.

The incident had made Hungarian Pete the butt of a long running joke on the wing. It was a position he appeared to be coping with until one evening he exploded in the TV room and nearly severed a man's ear with a metal dinner tray.

After that, as is the custom in any society where sudden assertion with the cutting edge of a steel tray is the ultimate arbiter, Hungarian Pete was no longer called 'Testicles', at least not within his hearing. Chuck and the Sheik made their peace with him, but he remained wary of their jokes, especially in the form of puns and verbal gymnastics. The man with the stitched-up ear was transferred to another wing, and shortly after to another prison. Hungarian Pete regained his composure, and became one of the characters of the Lazy L; a broad-faced, bald, stocky, jovial man who spoke an English of his own contrivance which was comprehensible with patience and goodwill.

We both attended the Current Affairs class once a week, and it was there, after a critical examination to see whether I was the sort who would play another trick on him, and being convinced I would not, he appointed me his tutor in English. I was pleased to accept; by that time I had come to appreciate his friendly engaging nature. There was another reason. It satisfied in me a sense of geometric pattern in inter-relationships; it seemed fitting that after two foreigners had humiliated a third, a fourth foreigner should be brought into play by the randomness of circumstance to rectify the balance. I am sorry to say that I did not rectify the balance.

Very soon after my appointment he converted me to his way of speech. I found it, as I had done that morning, more entertaining to visualize for instance, a cow's arse trying to hit a banjo, rather than the other way around.

It was mostly in the field of explaining phrases and current slang that I was helpful to him. So it did not surprise me that day as he nudged my shoulder conspiratorially and asked, "Who is a Anne's arse? Is he make a joke mith the bum?" he made a two finger gesture of entry towards his backside.

I told him I was reasonably sure it had nothing to do mith the bum, and rather more to do with political or military pastimes, but I was not sure. We went to my cell to find out.

There, from a seldom visited section of my bookshelf, I took down a once much consulted *Dictionary of Politics*. I read out what it said under ANZUS.

"Ho yes," Pete said. "I am an already know that."

The tutor in me was provoked.

"Ho no," I said. "You are a don't know before I am a tell you from a book. You are a think it was a joke mith the bum. You are a Seep." (Silly East European Person).

"If you are a call me Seep, I am a call you Sip," (Silly Indian Person) he said.

We started arguing about how long he had known about ANZUS, when he changed the subject.

"So vy is a man, Slippery, mith a hot voter pipe in his bum, jump up an run avay? I am a reckon myself, he vos a frightening from a blow up from Harry."

We discussed Slippery's change of heart. Why had he so suddenly called it off?

A few feet away across the landing, from Barry's cell, the Sheik and Chuck and a breathless Shaky who had won the contest with the screw, and still retained the half towel, were also conjecturing inconclusively about the events of the morning. Spurts of laughter of a certain unrestrained variety suggested they had lit the peace pipe early that day.

Footsteps at a pace that foretold a message stopped at Barry's open door. It was Dirty Harry.

"Thank fuck," he said. "You blokes are not going to believe this. We found the gear. It weren't up 'im at all. Never was! All of a sudden the soppy little cunt remembers where he put it. That's why he shot off like that in the middle of everythin'. It's been there all the time, in his cuntin' flower pot, would you believe! In among his cacti, for christsake!"

I was translating furiously for Pete while he kept demanding hoarsely in my ear, "Vot he say? Vot he say?" I maintained the other ear on Dirty Harry's story, and got the essentials of it.

The recent tightening up policy which had swept through the prison had affected all of us. The sudden gratuitous searches in the corridors, and at hitherto sacrosanct hours of the day of night, had made squirrels of us all; we hid anything that had to be hidden in the cleverest of unthinkable places. Slippery had been a squirrel all his life, perhaps due to the firm principles of larceny on which all his transactions were based. Now he became even more secretive.

He doubled his list of hiding places, and commuting freely between the fifth dimension and more accessible ones, not to mention astral projecting like crazy, he sometimes got confused, and forgot where he had put his valuables, imagining them to be one place when they were in another.

Before Hungarian Pete left that morning he paused at the door and said in his important announcement voice, "You can a mark up my vords, I am a never drink hot voter on a wing if a green pipe in his bum is comin' back on a boiler."

"I am an agree mith that," I said.

Repercussions

Large pink ears was unhappy about the group that had dispersed so suspiciously from the bath house. Australian Barry's presence, and reputation as an escape risk, influenced him to report the matter. That afternoon when the prisoners were locked up, the special crew called the 'burglars' stripped the bath house. They found no secret tunnels. The only item of escape equipment they found was a gallon of hooch behind the panels of the bath. It was a ten day vintage, and its loss displeased Mac the Brew enormously. They also found a five pound note. It was folded down to thumbnail proportions, and wedged behind a water pipe that disappeared into the floorboards. It could only be reached by a man on his hands and knees with his cheek pressed against the floor. The person who put it there must have slept soundly, imagining his property to be safe.

He used to. Its loss made me bankrupt.

The gymnasium, converted to a cinema hall, is full for the once weekly film. The members of the film committee are anxiously present; although they are reasonably confident that this evening's cultural entertainment will be well received.

The film centres around an armed robbery; two people get shot in good style; fountains of blood and gore issue forth, slow motioned by a thoughtful director, for maximum effect.

There is something for everybody; a bit of torture, violent rape scenes, stranglings, and an incident of child molesting. How can it miss?

It does not miss. The boys disband happily, calling out their approval to the now very visible film committee, and troop home. The ones racing back with glazed eyes are true life rapists, wishing to masturbate before the erection caused by the rape scenes have subsided.

The venue is one of Her Majesty's maximum security prisons in Britain.

There is a subtle and ingenious plan behind this carefully selected diet of dramatized crime, shown to actual criminals week after week. It is hoped it will produce a certain effect. The Penal Institution, and its policy makers at the Home Office, have a singular word to describe that effect: it is called, Rehabilitation.

Chapter 19

Meanwhile...

The blackboard that informed prisoners of special appointments had my name under the heading Education Office; it meant that I had to report there at 11.15 am. I imagined it was connected with the O level exam in Spanish, which I was due to sit for later that year.

In the annex to the Education office, a bearded officer in shirtsleeves seemed to know immediately I entered what I had been summoned for.

"Sign here, and escort that thing away," he said jocularly. He pointed to an area adjacent to the door I had entered. A large cardboard box whose flaps had been opened stood there, open mouthed.

I acted calmly enough, while emergency plans somersaulted around my brain.

This was Barry's box; and it was like going through the customs with contraband. The moment of truth was upon me.

"Um, yes, well, boom buddi boom," I murmured through a dry throat, as I fiddled with the proffered pen. I searched the man's face for a giveaway sign of precognition that he already knew what the box contained. There was none; he had gone back to his crossword puzzle.

I moved over to the box, and hefted it on to my shoulder. "Where's Carthage?" the officer asked abruptly.

I stood stock still, going cold. This was obviously a trick question; any ninny could see that; they already knew what was in the box and were playing a game of cat and mouse with me. I was just about to go into the verbal ritual that begins , "I do not wish to say anything until I have consulted..." when the door opened and another officer came in.

"...eight letters, ancient city, burned down," the bearded one said. As their heads leaned together poring over the crossword, I scuttled away crablike down the stairs, holding the prize clasped to my chest as though it was a big awkward child.

I curbed my feeling of relief by administering a correctional smack as it were to myself, for jumping at shadows. It had all been too easy, just as Barry had said it would. The box was in my possession; now all I had to do was carry it home.

My step was jaunty, and it is probable I whistled a martial tune, as I swaggered along through the centre, past the control room, busy as an antheap with screws going in and out. At the manually operated iron gates, a group of them exchanging inane opinions about rival football teams blocked my path.

"Let me pass there, gentlemen," I said imperiously. "I am on important business, carrying contraband for the Governor."

One of them opened the gate for me, and smiling, asked what was in the box.

"Grenades from the gallant Col Gaddafi," I said.

I heard him laughing as I passed through into the corridor. My feeling of satisfaction not to say elation increased with every step I took.

My thoughts had leapfrogged over several stages to when the successful sale of the illegal substances would make me solvent and creditworthy again. A feeling whose evocation alone, made me feel complacent and contented.

It was in that state of dreamy inaction that I heard a distant thunder which translated into a frothing-over of about a dozen screws through the iron gate I had just passed through. They gesticulated energetically, and braying confidently, charged towards me, some of them clutching their hats to their heads as they ran, in various stages of unfitness.

With reason, I was elevated back into a state of hypertension. This time I was sure they were after me, and the box; although an instinctive appreciation of my plight suggested there was something not quite plausible about the situation. Why would they go to these dramatic lengths; why had they not detained me at the office without any fuss, after I had signed for the box? There was no time to have a learned soliloquy on the subject; they were bearing down on me as fast as their illfitting blue suits and their precariously perched hats would allow them.

Like a bird caught in a net I was filled with fluttering indecision; but somewhere a seed of intelligence must have come to life; for I did not shoulder my box and madly gallop off down the dead end corridors blocked off at the end by a locked door, as my reflexes were urging me to do. Instead, I dropped the box on the floor, wrenched the flaps aside and dug my hands elbow deep into the polythene bag that held the foam rubber. At this point, it may have seemed that my behaviour was reminiscent of the large bird that is supposed to bury its head in the sand, in tense circumstances. My reasoning was sound enough; I was trying to locate just one small piece of foam rubber with a hard centre. If I were lucky enough to find one through my nervous groping efforts, I was going to abandon the box to the baddies, and while they were sniffing around it and wetting their trousers, as required by Home Office regulations, I would slink away down a convenient corridor, and either hide or throw the piece of foam rubber out of the window to be picked up later.

While these inspirational flashes were passing through me, the screws stampeded past me down the corridor that led to the workshops. One of their hat-clutching number, a man not cut out to be a front runner in any race, whose size and comportment would have enabled him to join a school of hippopotomi unnoticed, saw his chance to have a breather. He slowed down to a walk, and in a voice that was meant to suggest that he was in charge of the expedition, said, "Get that bloody box out of the way, will ya."

I nodded, bowed, scraped, and salaamed so profusely, that he was mollified, and nodded back at me quite amicably, before waddling off behind his colleagues.

Two false alarms one after the other had done my equilibrium no good, and I resolved to have a mug of tea and a poached egg on toast, as soon as I got back on the wing to calm myself down. I gathered up the spurts of foam rubber that had spilled over the top of the box due to my emergency plan, stuffed them back into the box, and carried it uneventfully back on to the wing. There a screw recently white-shirted, shook his head and smiled sadly.

"More sodding contraband coming on the wing, I suppose," he said.

There was a patina of seriousness around that joke. Just lately there had been presageful rumblings of discontent from some sections of the uniformed force. These men, used to, and approving of, a stricter regime for prisoners felt uncomfortable at the range of privileges allowed at the Lazy L; they wanted especially a much smaller list of items that prisoners were allowed to keep in their cells as personal property.

One piece of personal property I was glad to voluntarily relinquish that day was the box. Barry greeted the sight in the traditional style of macho men: he ducked and feinted and threw punches at my stomach and chest playfully yet forcefully.

"Nice one, sport. Nice one," he shouted in a voice that could be heard all along the landing. "Told you we 'd have these cunts over. Didn't I?"

I withstood his congratulations without wincing, and reflected in passing, that before I had come into prison such expressions of joy would have left me gasping. I told him of my incredible presence of mind not to say bravery during the transit of the box.

He laughed. "I told you, sport, that's not how these bastards work. If they'd 'a found it, you would never have known."

Barry wedged his door, and at my insistence pulled the bed across as a double barrier. We started to knead handfuls of foam, and if they squeezed authentically like foam rubber we put them into a pillow-case.

About a foot down into the box we had still encountered nothing to excite us. Barry paused and a look of annoyance as though he was reminded of something unpleasant formed on his face.

"I hope this bastard is not up to one of his clever games," he said.

I looked up at him for an explanation.

"You don't know this pal of mine," he continued. "It would be right up his street to turn a simple bloody thing into a complicated exercise. It would be just like him to send in a box with nothing in, as a dummy run."

The pressure of my excitement started to fall as though its vital supply had been cut off, and then with miraculous timing I felt something hard in my hot sweaty fist. I singled out one piece of pale blue foam, with stitching of an approximately similar colour bordering its edges, making a tiny envelope. I bit through the thread hurriedly, and out popped a small nut, covered in silver paper.

This was not a dummy run. For a few seconds we inspected it; evaluated its quality with the finger and nose method. It had an earthy, resinous odour, suggestive of another, lusher, climate.

"Temple ball," Barry whispered hoarsely. I could hear the exhilaration in his voice. "Hey! Hey! Hey!" he whooped loudly. "Keep diggin', sport, we're on our way."

By mutual consent, I stayed with the job, kneading and palpating handfuls of foam with the concentration of a man panning for gold; a simile that was apt, as gram for gram cannabis was literally more expensive in prison than gold was on the outside. Barry meanwhile, started to make a joint; the lighted match held under the lump released a familiar fragrance, that tickled my expectation.

A few seconds later I found another nugget, then a bunch of five close together, then two more, and so on, in no particular sequence; each one greeted with an inward spasm of delight. By the time Barry had made the joint, I had got through the box, which had produced thirty six nuggets, thirty seven, including the one we had unwrapped.

I put twelve in my pocket; Barry dealt a hand of draw poker to see who would get the odd one. After the badinage that is usual at these finalising transactions, I won with two small pairs, and added the slightly diminished thirteenth to my fortune. Each one I calculated was worth about ten pounds paper money, or seven pounds in silver, the official currency of the prison at that time.

When the doors had been locked for the hour between five and six, I wedged my door and luxuriated expansively in my mint condition of affluence. From pauper to rich man in one day; it was like winning the pools. I could dispense with tiring exercises at elusiveness. Lately I had acquired the reputation of having perfected the Indian rope trick and disappearing into thin air at the first glimpse of a creditor on the horizon. Indeed, I could now stand my ground, thumb my nose at those who had refused to extend my credit; I could face them nonchalantly, flipping coins of the realm into the air.

"How much do you say I owe you, my good man? Five pounds, eh? A trifling sum, old boy! Petty cash for a man in my position. Here's the five pounds, and here's a little something to put in your pipe tonight for being so patient."

The effect of the joint I had shared with Barry lapped around my consciousness, making me feel a little glazed; Temple Ball or not, it was certainly good quality black hashish. On a grading of one to ten which was the current expression of quality among aficionados at the lazy L, I would give it seven I thought; or there again, I might have to give it seven point five. When such uncertainty is in the air there is absolutely no reason whatsoever why one should not conduct further tests: which I did immediately, with another joint.

Lying three quarter length on the bed, my head and shoulders propped against the wall, smoking the joint and sipping hot tea, I filled my head with pleasant imagined incidents. The economic power I now wielded was the focal point of every one of them; notions which are so easy to propose and accept when one is balanced on the crest of success.

That hundred and thirty pounds of collateral I held in my palms gave me the same feeling of satisfaction, as the thousands I had made, on basically similar ventures outside. There was also a moral tone to this feeling; that somehow in however feeble a manner, I had fired a catapult shot at the giant ship of state, HMS Hypocrisy that made the use of cannabis criminal, while exhorting its citizens to maim and kill themselves, by licensing the sale of tobacco and alcohol on every street corner.

Chapter 20

The glorious 12th, as British an institution as you could wish for; the day when war is declared on a certain species of bird; an action taken unilaterally, and, of which the grouse is unaware, was also the day that began a time of trouble for me. It was 6 am on a brightening day of summer. I was into my fifth consecutive year in prison. The portents for parole were excellent; my co-defendants were all either out, or on parole. The first spasms of gate fever were affecting me; an unnameable apprehension of the future, mixed in with bouts of euphoria contemplating the diversity of one's choices.

My life had reached a comfortable plateau of existence at the Lazy L. I belonged suddenly, and recently, to the moneyed criminal classes. The first of Barry's foam rubber boxes had wiped out my debts and filled my cardboard box under the bed with the status symbols of convict life: bottles of honey, peanut butter, sardines, pilchards, coffee, packets of tea, biscuits, and fresh fruit. The second box moved me into the social grouping which above others invites envy and treachery: the nouveau riche. In the early stages of my life as a receiver of foam, rubber, I had tried to distance myself from the actual sale of the merchandise. I appointed two sales agents on other wings. They were on a twenty five per cent commission, or in simpler terms kept one out of every four single pound deals they sold.

I picked my men with my usual careful consideration of their qualities of taciturnity, and prudence. I cajoled them softly, then lectured them sternly, that the reason they were getting twenty five per cent was to keep the heat off me. My name, I said in a whisper, glancing over my shoulder for emphasis, should not, even under deep surgery, be revealed as the source of the golden eggs. That was their part; my part was to ensure the quality of the goods, and the size of the deals.

They promised me on their budgie's lives that they would honour that clause of the contract faithfully; their eyes shone with high fidelity. We shook hands in an atmosphere of saccharine sincerity, and parted tight-lipped.

I am unable to say for how many minutes and seconds my agents kept their end of the bargain.

What I am able to say is, that the next day I had achieved an overnight popularity; all sorts of strange guys I hardly knew were bumping into me in the corridors and public places of the Lazy L, and asking, with that revealing half smile that spells prior knowledge, if I had any dope to sell.

It tapped more securely into place the simple truth, that in a high security prison where men live for several years more or less in each other's pockets, there are no secrets. Gossip is the cheapest commodity.

At first I had denied being the owner, but it seems I did so with so much alacrity, protesting so emotionally, that they were convinced that I was. They pestered me daily, observing with sad reproachful eyes that large cloth bags filled with coins were being passed to me on pay day by my salesmen. These transactions, for reasons I never understood were always staged when the greatest number of people could take note of it. It became pointless to keep up my denials of complicity.

Even so, I was not unduly worried. There were in the Lazy L at that time, about a dozen prisoners who sold dope on a regular basis. They were all comfortably off in prison terms, and there was no sign of harassment from officialdom. The general feeling was that the authorities knew about the widespread use of cannabis in the prison; the opinion also was, that they preferred it that way.

Its effects ensured peace, or at least lessened the likelihood of violence. Those of us who had been convicted for cannabis offences and were in prison because of it, naturally discussed the question endlessly. One wistful conclusion we had come to, was that in twenty or thirty years' time, it would be the statutory duty of the penal institutions of the country to provide every prisoner with his ration of cannabis, in exactly the way he is entitled to receive his allocated portion of proteins and carbohydrates.

Everyone whom I had reason to be mindful of as a prisoner, and certainly everyone in uniform, had by their attitude sedated me into a belief that unless it was forcibly thrust up their nostrils, they were not going to take any action.

All the officers, of all three ranks, who were entrusted with the management of individual wings had to live with us day in and day out, year after year, as much as we had to live with each other. Dope made coexistence that much easier. C wing, where I had lived for four years had the ambience of a well ordered village; a tempo without tension. The citizens of that village, the ones in uniform, and the ones in T shirts and jeans, liked it that way.

About once a month two apologetic officers came to search us and cells. The procedure was for the prisoner to stay in the corridor with one of them, while the other searched the cell. Normally they stayed no longer than fifteen minutes, but even that short space of time left me dry-throated as I tried to pass the time of day with the screw outside; invariably I had a small piece of dope, not hidden so much as tucked away, somewhere in the cell. Usually the screw in the cell would unenthusiastically flick through a couple of books, or widen his horizon of sexual imagery by reference to the stack of girlie magazines under my bed. Then smiles of relief from *both* sides, and the search was concluded. When someone I knew, and had an individual relationship with like Taff, was on the search crew he used to put me high on the list of prisoners to be searched; but the only searching he did was of my world map taped to the wall. After the search had been abandoned before it had got started, we played our geographical quiz game. The other screw usually ended up as the referee.

That was the spirit of the Lazy L I had become used to. It all ended at 6 am on the glorious twelfth; the grouse and I fell to the first salvo, victims of policy changes we had not been told of.

The door opened, not preceded by the customary knock but suddenly, aggressively. The small single cell was full of uniforms; there were only three of them, but they seemed to have filled every corner and crevice of that room. Sharp eyes were taking in all the objects in the cell. My own eyes were bleary, my brain in about the same state.

"Spin, Krishnamma." I heard the bleached tones of law-enforcement and a weakening nausea formed in my stomach.

I moved slowly, trying to engage my brain into a coherent gear.

"Are these your clothes?" It was the same featureless voice.

I grunted something unintelligible, my mind desperately trying to remember what I had done with the remains of the piece of dope I had smoked the night before. It was only a tiny piece, about a gram in weight and it was loose somewhere in that cell, and I didn't know where. My main stock I had buried outside.

"Did you hear me? Are these your clothes, sunshine?" The voice now had notches of sarcasm in it. This is quite consistent with investigative minions of a certain type; after a time they believe they invented the laws they enforce, and come to feel about them as if they were private property.

I looked at the voice to identify his features. It was nobody I knew, although I had seen him a few times; he was new at the Lazy L.

His mentality was reflected in the way he wore his hat. It was intentionally several sizes too small for his close-cropped blond head, which conveniently allowed him to wear it in the style of his favourite Gestapo officer on films, so that the peak shaded his eyes. To look anyone in the face he had to tilt his head back. This manoeuvre was intended to give the impression of a tough, mean, and dangerous agent. A sullen girl's mouth, and a little pointed chin, denied him his fantasy.

"Don't," I said, while in my head I heard the articulation of my own voice whispering urgently, "What the fuck have you done with the ganja you fool?"

"Don't what?" His head was inclined backwards as he watched me get out of bed in my underpants.

"Don't call me sunshine," I said. "You know my name."

His condescending attitude faltered, as if he had been tripped. "Never mind about that," he said. "Just drop your underpants."

"I will not," I said reaching for my trousers, which one of the one of the others was kneading along the line of the stitching, to see if there was anything sewn in.

"I am giving you a direct order to drop your underpants." The voice now had the tonality of a ritual I had heard before. I knew my part of the incantation quite well, as its usage had cost me several weeks remission at Winchester.

At the Lazy L, that response had not been necessary until now.

"And, I'm giving you a direct refusal. No, I will not."

"That's up to you. I'm nicking you for refusing a direct order. We've got orders to search you, *and* this cell thoroughly, so if you've got anything to declare, do it now."

I didn't answer, just put my denims on, while in my head the same momentous question rolled around like a stone in an empty drum. Memory struggled and writhed like an animal caught in a trap, but came up with nothing. A casual yet penetrating glance around the room, especially on the cluttered chair serving as a bedside table had no results. Like the system gambler who in desperation abandons the percentages, to let fate decide his fortune, I gave up trying to remember where I had put it, and inspired myself to believe that if I couldn't find it, they wouldn't either; it was after all, less than a gram in weight and would look like a small clod of earth brought in on my shoes. I consoled myself that that is what had happened; it had fallen on the floor, and would by its unmasked prominence not be recognized for what it was.

The next order was not so contentious; it was to take my bedclothes outside the cell and wait there with one of them; the leader and the other one stayed in the cell to search it. The screw who came out with me was pleasant enough; he didn't bother with my bedclothes, but looked quickly in my shoes, tapping them first, on the floor, then said, "I suppose it won't do me any good to ask you to open your mouth?"

His tone was expressive of a man engaged in a task he was disinclined to perform. His attitude was not only different from his colleagues, it was intended to be seen to be so. I wondered if it was a permutation of the hard guy, soft guy teams that police department find effective. One shouts and threatens; the other appeals, even flatters.

"Since you put it like that, listen carefully," I said. "'The rain in Spain falls mainly on...' and 'She sells seashells by the seashore'."

I enunciated the words clearly as though for an audition

"We'll call you, don't call us," he said, then added. "What was it in aid of?"

"It was a short demonstration to show you I had nothing hidden in my mouth," I said. "No offence and nothing personal intended, but I only allow my bank manager and dentist to look down my throat, usually with painful consequences."

Later that week I was to regret my flippancy. A hotchpotch version of all that I had said that morning was regurgitated at my 'trial'. In the telling it sounded like congenital arrogance; in truth it was an instinctive defence mechanism over which I had not too much control. My effusion was as natural as putting my hand up to ward off a blow; it was born of fear and tension, and not as interpreted by my captors, as premeditated effrontery. Its effects had caused me trouble throughout my sentence.

After an hour, as the regular officers on the wing were assembling for the 7 o'clock general unlocking, the search was ended. I was ordered to step back into the cell to be faced by the misplaced stormtrooper who got his last thrill out of the situation. What he did then, was so in keeping with my assessment of his mentality, that in spite of my position in the drama, it gave me a hopeless sort of satisfaction to know that I had detected from the iceberg tilt of his hat, the mass of ordinary human meanness that lay beneath.

He had laid out on the bed three items. My assurance grew perceptibly. Two of them infringed the rules of prison in very minor ways. At the Lazy L those rules were not enforced. The third was puzzling, but of no consequence; if that was all I had to worry about, I had nothing to fear.

"This?" He pointed, and I visualized the imaginary cane, to the first of the exhibits.

It was a small penknife, about 5 cm long, owned jointly by Tiger Bay as an onion-slicing tool. Its existence, and common ownership was known in the wing office.

I explained all that to him.

"We'll see," he said. "This is all excess kit," he pointed at an assortment of socks, underwear, towels and plastic cutlery.

I nodded, and said nothing. My attention was held by the third item. It was a small Nescafe bottle nearly full of dogends. They were there to treat the sporadic bouts of bankruptcy fever which afflicted me.

The level of the bottle declared that recently the illness had not assailed me. My spirits floated a little higher. There was nothing but stale tobacco in the dogends; if I had any roaches to dispose of, I made sure they were shredded before they went out of the window.

"Dogends for a rainy day," I said.

"Yeah, I can see that," he smirked elaborately. "What's in them?"

"A narcotic, and highly addictive drug that is a convicted killer on a mass scale, that should be banned, called tobacco." I said. My confidence had fully returned. I felt the bounce of relief and satisfaction that comes when an unforeseen and potentially dangerous hurdle is successfully crossed; it was exactly the way he wanted me to feel. It is always more stimulating for the hunter to let the bird feel it is flying to freedom, before he shoots it down. While I spoke he was watching my face intently, and the undisguised look of triumphant spitefulness that grew in his eyes made the words stall on my lips.

He engineered a moment of silence then, like the breathless second before a wave rears back to launch itself on the shoreline. I knew in that space of time, even though he had not spoken, just by the expression on his face, that I was lost.

"And this is also a drug, an illegal one I believe," he said, opening his loosely closed right hand. This was his moment, and no doubt in his head the trumpets of denouement sounded sweetly. He was Sherlock Holmes confronting Moriarty or James Bond in the final victorious scene with the king of the bad men.

A proposed mental reflex careered around my head; if I made a sudden lunge for his hand, maybe I could just snatch that incriminating black marble away from him, and swallow it. Even as I thought it, he closed his fist.

"Do you want to tell us anything about it?" he asked, making an unsuccessful effort to sound legal and dispassionate.

I swallowed the dryness away from my throat. A weakening disorientation enveloped me as though this was just a bad dream, and an effort of will would bring me back to routine normality, and knowing again even as I thought it, that this was no dream. My life had changed in a few minutes. An hour ago in half sleep I had been buoyantly imagining how I would restart my life after an absence of five and a half years. So much to do, so much adventure left. I had, during that hour-long search frittered away another two years of my life; there would be no parole now. And consistent with other landmarks in my life, I had achieved this state of affairs through carelessness and complacency.

His voice interrupted my whirling thoughts. "I said, is there anything you want to tell us, about it?" he asked again.

The fact that he felt he could ask me that question kicked my spirit awake. He had broken into my life's storehouse and stolen two years from it; now the thief in a cosy, after-the-event chat, wanted me to describe and locate other doors through which he could make further raids on other storehouses: I wanted to dredge up from some deep part of me the spittle of contempt and gob it on his face; and at least a half of that anger would have been for my own stupidity.

But instead, I said, "Yes, there's quite a bit I can tell you about it. For a start it's cannabis, probably what is known as Border Black, that is the border between Afghanistan and Pakistan, you understand. Now, if you will just bring it out here again, I'll show you how to make a joint—quite a tricky operation as you will see; the pity is, one has to poison it with tobacco, making a joint. Better to pipe it, or eat it. I've been using it for twenty five years and believe I am a better human being for it, etcetera, etcetera."

"That wasn't what I meant." He had listened to my panegyric, stone-faced. "What I'm asking is, where did you get it? Did you bring it in on a visit, or did you buy it in the nick?"

"Don't be so silly, I know exactly what you meant," I said, and then, "what happens now?"

What happened then, was that I was escorted to the punishment block; a drab descending journey of stairs, and empty, early morning corridors, to the central, most fortified part of the Lazy L; a small prison within a prison.

On the way down, Gestapo and the colleague who had searched the cell with him walked a few paces behind; the other pleasanter one kept step with me.

As we passed the wing office, I caught a reflected glimpse in the glass window of Gestapo punching the air with a clenched fist, as a footballer does in his moment of victory. That gesture of triumph to a crony getting ready to come on duty whom I could not see, somehow made me feel better. Deriving so much pleasurable mileage as he was from the incident, made me feel important; in this play I was the star, and he the bit player.

Thoughts and observations speeded up by the circumstances beyond individual recognition while it was happening crystallized later in the block, when time was elongated to many times its normal capacity. It was also in the block on that first day, that I realised that the innovative aspects of what is a fairly structured game were over; the moment when I could have snatched the evidence away from him with a quick desperate lunge, and so to alter the rules, had ended; now the pretentious, procedural part called British Justice in Prisons, was about to begin.

Chapter 21

The cell I was shown into brought back memories of being in police custody; it was liberally inscribed with the graffiti hopes and aspirations of those who had been there before me.

There was a 'Rules for Prisoners' booklet telling them of their rights, neatly packaged in cellophane, propped up on the pillow of the bed.

I took it over to the window, got it out of its nest, and tore it up into strips, made the strips into darts and floated them into the tiny exercise yard. This action had always been a calling card of mine in any punishment block.

"I knew it was you as soon as I saw the aeroplanes comin' out the window. What's up?"

The words connected my thoughts to David's face and I imagined him half smiling two cells away. His periodic, seemingly futile, attempts to escape made him an almost permanent resident of the punishment block. It was an address of which he was quite proud. I told him of the sequence of events that had landed me in his company.

"Nothing to worry about," he said airily. "Probably get a fine, or a week's remission taken off you. They know the nick's full of gear. Might have been a bit different if the foam rubber thing had come on top."

Spontaneous alarm bells went off in my head. "What foam rubber thing?" I asked trying to keep my voice conversational, and unconcerned. Until that second, perhaps because of the successful delivery of two boxes, I had persuaded myself to believe that Barry and I were the only ones who knew about the foam rubber scam.

"Talk to you later on exercise," David said, as a screw opened the door with a key (the electronics of the rest of the prison did not include the punishment block).

I turned away from the window, painful knots of frustration, and anger were tightening in me. I was trying to figure out if the search that morning was an ad hoc outing, or whether it was the end result of a deeper investigation concerning the foam rubber. There was no way of knowing how much the authorities at the Lazy L knew. How did David who had been in the block for at least two months, supposedly in isolation, know so much about it? Obviously it had come from Barry, since I had not mentioned it to anyone.

At 9.30 the doors were opened for exercise. There was one other person in the block; a man of about fifty, lost in a private recording studio of his own, singing the first lines of 'That ole black magic', over and over again as though he were reciting a mantra.

"Nutter," David said, as we started walking around the yard.

"So what's this about foam rubber?" I asked.

"I heard you and Barry had this thing going with boxes of foam rubber," he said.

"Where did you hear that?"

David, immediately evasive, started to mumble, and swing his arms about in an unconvincing outbreak of callisthenics. I heard him mutter the words 'prison rumour', and knew he wasn't going to give me any names.

By complicated questions I managed to wheedle out of him that it was about as well known a story at the Lazy L, as Kennedy's assassination.

Later, when I got up into the daylight of normal prison, I was to learn that half the prison had known about it, soon after the first box had arrived. Barry, show-off to the core, had boasted to fellow book makers on other wings, that he had found a foolproof method of getting dope into the Lazy L.

After a few glasses of hooch and a joint or two, for further acclamation, he told them how it was done. From that day it was no longer foolproof. If I had known about that breakage in our vows of silence, I would have declared my name unavailable for subsequent parcels; I would have been thankful that the first one had got through, and lifted me out of debt.

Walking around that sunny yet forlorn little concrete yard, the sound of 'That ole black magic' as inspirational music for my thoughts, I knew by now the authorities at the Lazy L must know of it. The Lazy L, like every other prison in Britain, had its share of grasses, men whose obsession for getting out on parole, or even a transfer to another prison, overwhelmed all notion of loyalty to the criminal brotherhood—a largely fictional fellowship anyway.

I pictured scenes of confrontation with Barry, and the subsequent unpleasantness; my stomach turned over with frustration, to get it over with.

It was all needless exertion; I was never to see the wild Australian Barry Goodwin again.

It was decided that my charge was grave enough to be considered by a VC (visiting committee) of magistrates. Having always met such people in their professional capacity, in unequal relationships, and having also met their elder brother the judge, and having been at the receiving end of his bad humour, I could only hope that my adjudicators would be in a friendly mood on that morning.

They were to meet in four days; in the meantime I was remanded in the block to await their pleasure, and exhibitions of justice and wisdom.

The day before they were to assemble, word came down to the block through the cleaners, that Barry had been 'shanghaid' for reasons unknown, to a destination unknown.

The story was that it had all been planned carefully; Barry was pounced on while he was on his way to the gym. Clad only in his shirt and vest; one version had it that he had been carted away spitting, and struggling, the other that he had gone quietly to the waiting prison van. What was certain was that he was gone. I was relieved that our relationship had ended on that anticlimax. Later, when I heard how fortune had played its trump card on his life, I was even more glad of it.

After serving twelve years of a fourteen-year sentence Barry Goodwin was released from the care of Her Majesty's prisons in England. He was deported back to Australia. Within a week of his arrival in Melbourne, he had been shot dead in the heat of what was described as a domestic dispute. Those of us who had heard his zig-zagging monologues of hatred, and revenge, against one-time friend, and one-time mistress; soliloquies of such grave intent, that had matured into firm committments, during the long brooding prison days and nights, could imagine how his plans might have backfired on him.

Chapter 22

On the morning of the adjudication, an hour or so before the big event, a Principal Officer came to instruct me on how I should conduct myself.

The props and dramatic instructions were minimal. I was to wear black prison issue shoes, not sandals, button up my shirt, stand squarely on the plastic, which I was assured would be in situ, and when given the cue, announce my name and number. There was a problem, I had no shoes. "No problem," he said. Presently a pair of shoes, several sizes larger than my requirements arrived; with them was a pair of socks.

I threw the socks out of the window, put the shoes on, and sat down on the edge of the bed to think out some sort of battle plan. I practised several notes of penitence, and misery. "Krish sob namma, 43 sob 5598", and so on. My acting ability I knew could not cope with such demands, and I discarded that idea.

Perhaps the sight of a poor prisoner without socks, and shoes that flopped about like flippers, might wring those parts of a magistrate's heart that had never been wrung before; I thought. I wondered if magistrates and judges, and all the other echelons in the punishing business, wondered about their victims as much as those waiting in the cells, wondered about them. What would they be like? Tall? Short? Bald? Hairy? Overflowing with compassion? Cold as statues? Might one, or all of them, in earlier student days, have tasted of the virtues of cannabis, and take a dismissive view of my charge? There are no lower limits to the size of straws prisoners will clutch at, when waiting to be he sentenced.

The Principal Officer came back to say they were ready.

"What are they like?" I asked.

"Bad," he said. "Two of them got knuckle dusters, and the third has a bicycle chain around her neck."

"Thanks," I said. "That's put a bit of heart into me. I'll make a note of your name, and see if I can put in a good word for you while I am in there."

He thanked me, and I entered the room. There were three of them; in the middle a large pyramid shape, thinly disguised as a lady in a green hat, wearing small round glasses, glared at me powerfully over them. She was a dominating physical presence. I guessed she must have weighed about as much as a full grown kangaroo; the comparison came easily as she was built like one. Seven eighths of her was bum and legs, both massive, and ebbing over the seat of her chair. It seems she had not shaved too well that morning. A plum coloured chin would not be subdued by makeup. Hope ran out of me like water down a drain, as I saw how that chin was set; it gave my prisoner's heart no comfort whatsoever. Her expression conveyed, it seemed to my petrified eyes, a general malevolence towards everyone, and a more specific one toward me. The man on her right was a sporty, bibulous-looking elder citizen in a blazer, much embuttoned with yellow metal. It was also much showered with tobacco ash. The underside of his white moustache was tinged ochre. In his hands he held a Benson & Hedges packet which he was rolling over in his palms, as though he was trying to judge its weight.

I guessed he could be a retired naval officer, who probably drove a personally tuned MG. He wore a permanent half smile on his face. I felt that whatever his values may be, I had half a chance of leniency with him. But it seemed to me, the shadow of the Pyramid engulfed him completely.

The other lady was small, and totally forgettable; a composite of nondescript features. I remember a mousey aura, from a grey phantom. In my mental calculations she too seemed completely daunted by the physical majesty of the Pyramid. These three were to be my judges. As references, I thought of them as Cheops, The Admiral, and Mousey.

I disregarded the other two and concentrated on Cheops. At another suitably less executive table, Peter Quinn and the Chief, Mr Porter, sat with my file. The size of that file made my knees wobble a bit. It was so *thick*. What the hell were they saying about me in there? There was no time to worry about it, but my self assurance such as it had been, plunged to zero. In desperation I fixed brown eyes on Cheops' glinting blue ones; my master plan was to establish a bridge between them, and then send over it emotional pleas for mercy.

As I was pondering how to achieve this intricate piece of chemical engineering, I was asked to give my name and number. It seems that in the excitement of the moment I had not noticed that I was already standing on the grey plastic mat.

I suppose I must have delivered my lines comprehensively enough, as I was asked to sit down. I maintained eye contact with Cheops, and continued to gaze soulfully at her. At a seated level, she had exposed to my view a formidable pair of knees, the size of most people's buttocks.

Gestapo was the spokesman for the three officers who had searched my cell, and he began a spirited recital of my wrong doing. As he spoke, Cheops' eyes shifted from me to him and then back to me, as if for confirmation that this abject creature with the olive oil eyes, in Charlie Chaplin shoes, sitting in front of her, could have committed such a dastardly deed.

Each time she looked at me I tried to produce a small regretful smile of acceptance; a visual effect that would encapsulate the message that yes, I was guilty of this monstrous crime, but honestly Cheops my beloved, it was spur of the moment madness, totally out of character for a sober and responsible citizen/criminal of a high security prison, such as I was. My mind, normally so gainfully occupied with thoughts of larceny, fraud, or violence, had somehow this time slipped a gear; it had sought the forbidden thrills of tranquility and peace; it had in the solitude of my cell at night, tried to implement those gross desires. What can I say now, Cheops my little one, except that I bitterly regret my moment of weakness. I shall from this day forth (if you are merciful, that is), exile from my mind all thoughts of ever ingesting this evil weed again.

Complicated as this wordless message was, I felt a quick sense of recognition that Cheops was getting some part of it. One has to know a bit about the as yet unwritten book called, 'How to influence people with looks and glances', to interpret these signs correctly.

Her eyes so ablaze with righteous displeasure seemed to be softening, wavering. The arched outrage of her eyebrows seemed to have lost their curvature of annoyance. And was there not evidence of disquiet in the way she tugged her skirt over those prize-winning pumpkin knees?

I was getting through to her, by God. Speechlessly, solely through the entreaty of my eyes, and the heartrending petition of my smiles, and grimaces, I had won the Pyramid over to my side. Now she would speak powerfully on my behalf; quell any difference of opinion from the others, and jointly they would pass a lenient sentence on me.

My parole chances would not be jeopardized, and all would be well.

This is the way every prisoner sees his chances of escaping the inevitable grinding end of the bureaucratic machine that deals with Law and Order. He never ceases to believe in miracles; to do so would be to curl up and die, for there can be no thought of winning against the machine. He must learn to play these mind games to survive, to learn to prolong hope indefinitely through imagination, however wild or fanciful those thoughts might be.

In truth, his fate has already been decided; nothing innovative or startling is going to be said or done at his trial to make matters better for him. And there is always the possibility that they might get worse.

The next stage of the ritual buffoonery got under way. Gestapo, looking flushed and important, had finished. I was asked if I would like to ask him any questions.

I declined the invitation. Gestapo looked disappointed, almost as if I were not playing the game; as if I were taking all the fun out of the party. He had envisaged no doubt, a scenario of verbal cut and thrust between the wily, oriental, master criminal, and the young, clean cut, and dedicated detective.

As a matter of fact, the wily oriental master criminal had at that moment been struck by a futuristic concept. It was the sort of idea that is born in circumstantial heat, but one which impresses even then, in passing, as being worthy of elaboration later on.

It was this: that one day as the societies of the world grew more mature and just, the act of punishing people who did not conform, would be taken away from human beings and given to computers. Once someone had been found guilty, (even that could be accomplished by a clever machine) or had pleaded guilty voluntarily, machine intelligence could take over. The victim himself could have the honour of twiddling the knobs and dials, and out would pop a little card that said, 'Go to prison for ten years, death penalty cards could be tastefully edged in black. Courtrooms and other venues of adjudication would never again have to face the horrendous sight of magistrates and judges weeping copious tears, sobbing their hearts out, as they passed sentence on the prisoner in the dock.

The whole of that trauma could be passed on to a machine. We ordinary mortals don't appreciate the enormous strain these kindly souls are subjected to. Every day of their working lives they have to inflict retributive justice in the name of the state. Punish! Punish! Punish! It is no wonder that occasionally some of them crack up, and pass a compassionate sentence on the son or daughter of somebody important.

While I was thinking these important thoughts on how to change the societies of the world, Peter Quinn began to read out a report of my conduct on the wing.

Everything he said seemed to support my now growing conviction that I would get off lightly. I had been a model prisoner, he said, well liked by the staff and fellow prisoners alike; cooperative and helpful in the affairs of the wing, I had never before been placed on report for anything.

The four years I had spent at the Lazy L had been without blemish. I shot meaningful, I told you so glances at Cheops, to see if she was taking note. I was pleased to see that she was writing something down as he spoke.

So the programme inched forward. Nearly an hour had elapsed. Finally in an atmosphere of shuffling feet, and straightening backs, the kind that attends the intermission of a cultural bill of fare, I was asked if I had anything to say. I said I did.

That was a terrible mistake.

Optimism, that flower capable of growing in the poorest soil was blooming in me. So far, nothing had been done or said, to scare me. The proceedings had been low key, matter of fact; there had been no thunderous denunciations, no passionate pleas from the prosecution for my head. David had been right, there was nothing to worry about here; just a minor transgression being dealt with by adjudicators eager to get to the local before lunch, on a warm August morning.

I felt I could oblige and enlighten these good people. A short educational lecture on the nature and after effects of cannabis, with an odd historical fact, and maybe a little humorous rhetoric was what was called for; something light and witty, but veined with truth.

So, I blundered in, waving a crumpled piece of paper on which I had the previous night jotted down some notes, taken from Playboy magazine an American institution that espouses the cause of legalizing cannabis.

I told them that cannabis had been used as a harmless relaxant for thousands of years, all over the world. Then, hoping the researchers of Playboy had got their facts right, that until 1947 its usage had been legal in Britain; that the Warren Commission on Drug Abuse in America, and the Royal Commission on Drugs headed by Barbara Wooton in England, had both concluded that its usage should be legalized. Repeated investigations into the effects of commonly used narcotics had established beyond doubt that it was far less harmful than tobacco or alcohol. Did they know that 100,000 lives were lost each year in Britain alone from the effects of tobacco smoking? As I said the word tobacco, I paused to indicate with a derisory flourish of my paper, and a barbed look, the Benson & Hedges packet the Admiral was toying with. I registered with a slight sense of consternation that my panel of judges were inspecting me with the vacant, yet curious gaze of tourists standing before a strange monument, whose inscription they could not decipher. They were not listening to me.

So, I blundered on further, and deeper. Did they know I asked them, brandishing my paper, as if delivering a clever punchline, that their own illustrious Queen Victoria had by her own admission been a user of cannabis? One of the less controversial duties that John Brown had to perform was making hemp tea for the Queen when the dreaded PMT set in. Did they know that?

Apparently they did not; nor did they wish to know about the eccentricities of the British monarchy. They indicated this to me not in so many words, but by that same glazed stare of sightseers who have seen too many broken down statues, and piles of stones, to comprehend that one of them was trying to speak. So, I blundered on in a different direction. The worst aspect of this charge, one that would certainly be brought up when possible sentences were being discussed, was the nature of my offence. There I was, at the finishing end of a ten-year sentence for a cannabis-related offence (the highest ever passed on anyone at that, time in England). Now I had been charged yet again while actually serving that sentence in prison, with another similar, albeit, lesser charge. I had learned nothing. What else could this be construed as but hardline defiance, or stupidity.

I wanted to offer them preemptive mitigation. "Consider this," I said. "Prisoners doing a sentence for a cannabis offence are in an unusual position in British prisons. The man convicted of bank robberies, and sent to prison for it, has no chance of repeating his crime there; there are no easy Barclays or National Westminster banks to tempt him on his way to work at the mailbag shop. The rapist and the child-molester have the objects of their desire denied them in prison. There is also no market whatsoever for passing stolen travellers cheques in prison. But the man convicted of a cannabis offence is taken from the frying pan, and thrust into the fire of temptation.

Cannabis, marijuana, hashish, dope, whatever you want to call it, is part of our lives in prison; it is as much of an alternative currency in British prisons today, as tobacco ever was. It is used every day as an instrument of pleasure, and commerce. Purchases are made with it; debts are settled with it, and favours bought with it. It is as much money to us here in prison as real money is to you people outside. I didn't create this situation.

It was already like this before I arrived here. Every prison I have been in, or heard of, is like this.

There was a guttural clearing of throats, exasperated hissing sounds, and chair scraping noises from the section that seated the prison officers. I understood all that to be an amorphous expression of their disagreement, or displeasure at what I was saying. But I was in full, irreversible flight, heedless of propriety, or danger. I blundered on.

A man convicted of a cannabis offence and sent to prison for it, especially someone who is a user himself, is comparable to a person with a sweet tooth sentenced to work in a sweet shop. Temptation walks with him the whole day long. Why, if there were any equity in the world, if natural justice prevailed, I should be rewarded for the four years I had lived in the prison without being charged."

I rounded off my speech with a resounding prediction. "Just you wait and see, I warned, a courtroom such as this in a few years time would not be convening to discipline a prisoner for smoking cannabis; its purpose would be to listen to his complaint that he is not getting enough of it. The law will be changed. You can't kid the people for ever. And let me tell you something else; the giants of commerce, well known by their brand names, are waiting in the wings licking their commercial lips, in anticipation of the time when they can market the stuff.

"All they are waiting for is the green light, and the supermarkets will be full of cannabis tea, courtesy of Twining and Tetley, not to mention packets of Marlboro and Benson & Hedges with (as per governmental regulations), the per cent of cannabis printed on the side, right under the bit that says smoking tobacco is bad for your health."

At this point my eloquence stumbled badly. I caught sight of Peter's face, and as our eyes met he winced and as in pantomime, closed his eyes, and turned his head toward the ceiling. It was some sort of advisory gesture. But what exactly was the message? Had I gone in too strong, and over the top? Should I try to retract some of what I had said with a quick, "I was only joking, folks". I didn't know what to do. I became confused. Like a runner afflicted with sudden cramp I shuddered to a stop, and limped off the verbal track.

I was then told to leave the room, and was escorted out; the panel of judges stayed, to debate the most suitable punishment for me. The Admiral was lighting up thankfully as I left. David was on exercise and hurried over to the bars of my window, as he heard my cell door bang shut. He was less than encouraging when I told him how my trial had gone. About my speech in mitigation he was more forthright. He burst into a cynical chuckling laugh.

"You've just shit on yourself from a great height," he said. "That's not what they want to hear at all. They want to hear how sorry you are, and you won't do it again, and all that crap. They want you to plead and beg with them, mate. You'd a done better if you'd said nothing, stayed stoom. The last thing they want to hear is some clever arse, especially an Indian clever arse demanding his rights, telling them what should be legal and what shouldn't, in their own country. You'll be lucky if you don't get another ten years for this lot."

In my head I dismissed his opinion as being of no account. He was obviously jealous of my public speaking ability. It would be my turn to laugh when I was called back into the room, and dismissed with a caution not to do it again. My optimism envisaged a commendation from the panel on how well I had presented my case. They might even want to have an informal chat with me when the court had been adjourned. They must surely want to know what life was really like in prison, from an inmate's point of view.

David, perforce, had a jaundiced opinion of visiting magistrates. He had in fact finished his actual prison sentence of seven years, and was currently finishing off the time he had lost in prison for a variety of offences; the largest chunks were for leading roles in prison riots, and trying to escape. He had managed to get his name into the Guinness Book of Records for having taken part in the biggest breakout from a prison in Britain (Brixton-London). He hated anything that strutted around in a uniform; a hatred that expressed itself in fearsome violence at times. It was no wonder that visiting magistrates gave him the big stick whenever they saw him. I could easily imagine the effect his bored indifference to the proceedings would have had on his judges, trying as they were, to give their shabby little ad hoc court room a high judicious tone.

I, on the other hand, was another bunch of bananas I told myself. I had no record of violence. My offences in prison had been small ones, mainly refusing to go to work, and once for being in possession of 2 lb of corned beef, stolen out of the kitchen. They had asked me if I had anything to say, and I had said it. I had spoken forthrightly, frankly. It was up to them to evaluate what I had said, to check the references I had made, if they were interested in the truth. They surely could not punish me more severely than they would have done if I had said nothing. I had not been tried for being a clever arse Indian with views contrary to the law of the land. I had been tried for being in possession of a tiny piece of cannabis, less than a gram in weight. Now what could they possibly do to me for that?

I consoled myself in this way as I stood talking to David; yet I could not rid myself of the memory of Peter Quinn's grimace of discomfiture, nor the tone of certainty with which David had said I had shit on myself from a great height.

Just as these mixed feelings were making me feel a little fragile, I heard a sound which lifted my spirits somewhat. The discussion among the magistrates as to how best to chastise me had so far not been audible to us, but then suddenly an eruption of laughter reached our ears. It was a spontaneous, hearty sound of good cheer. I immediately concluded naturally, that any bunch of people who were in that mood, who could laugh so joyously, could not pass a vindictive, exemplary, or harsh sentence on some poor wretch in outsize shoes, a few minutes later.

David had a different opinion. He said I was too naive for this world, let alone prison. Laughter, loaded with malice, was the trademark of visiting magistrates he said. He had personal experience he added, of them laughing and joking exuberantly minutes before they made a U-turn emotionally, and passed a heavy sentence on him.

At that moment as if on cue, peals of laughter issued forth again; a short silence then more rounds of ebullient laughter came through. They were having a great time in there. Whatever they were laughing about, I could detect no venom in the sound.

"Did you hear that?" David asked. "You've had it, old son. I've sat in more blocks waiting for the VC's decision than you've had cups of tea. I'm telling you, I know that sound. They're just working themselves up. They are going to *slaughter* you when you get back in there."

I did not want to believe that. But what the hell were they laughing about? What, in fact, was there to laugh about? I was waiting, in extreme apprehension, for what they were about to say to me. My life was going to be affected by those words. If the charge was as serious as had been made out earlier, how could they laugh about it?

It could only mean, I consoled myself, that the charge and sentence were so inconsequential, that they could have a little laugh on the side. I could not begrudge them a little light relief, even if it was at my expense so long as the eventual outcome was satisfactory.

Perhaps the Admiral was recounting some of his naval experiences. Then, wishfully, I imagined it may have been a remembrance of the ingenious, humorous manner, in which I had presented my mitigation, that evoked such goodnatured laughter? Surely, the sound I had heard could not have been anything but a harbinger of good news?

Just as the tension within me was mounting to fingernail-biting proportions, the door was opened and I was beckoned out into the charge room again.

This time, two sizable prison officers flanked me, as I stood quivering, on the grey plastic mat.

Prison history has it, that the number of Visiting Magistrates who got hurt after passing their sentences, had reached an unacceptable level. The two bulky screws on either side of me were there to ensure that the level was not increased.

Then, in a flat upper class accent, in which there was no laughter present, the Pyramid pronounced the sentence.

The essence of what she said was that this was a grave and despicable crime I had committed. Since their statutory powers did not allow them to have me decapitated, castrated, or thrust into boiling oil instantly, they would do the best they could under the circumstances, which was that I was to spend fourteen days in the punishment block, and lose a hundred and twenty days' remission.

The points I had raised in mitigation, and on which I had banked so much, were not referred to at all.

I felt a firm compelling pressure on my back and upper arms. I was being trundled out of the room by the two screws on either side of me.

There was no time to wave goodbye, or blow a kiss to Pyramid and the others, or take a bow, before I was whisked away and heard, as in a dream, the door slamming behind me.

A few minutes later David was returned to his cell after his period in the gym. In those few minutes he had already been told what my sentence had been. There are no jungle drums, or smoke signals, as fast as the system of news dissemination that operates in prison; especially if the news is bad for someone else.

Through his commiserations, shouted to me, from a few windows away, at an angle at which I could not see him, I detected an astringent whiff of, "I told you so." In my mood of numbed dejection it did not matter.

Later, through a long night of intermittent sleep, the actual cost of what had happened to me trickled through.

First, there was the sentence itself. Fourteen days in the punishment block was no great hardship. I had done other periods in the punishment block of other prisons, and the regime in the block at the Lazy L was an easy one. It would just be boring, not arduous.

The loss of a hundred and twenty days' remission was an excessive sentence to accept for the possession of a small piece of cannabis the size of a pea. Still, I would have suffered that with a smile, well almost a smile; four *extra* months in prison was a big pill to swallow, even though I had by then over five years practice at it.

It was the second, spin off, consequence that hurt so much; the one that dug so deeply into my hopes and aspirations was that I had destroyed all chances of parole.

The statutory right of all prisoners doing over three years, except lifers, is that they may apply for parole after a third of their sentences have elapsed. This carrot, called parole, is dangled before all the donkeys in prison. And like donkeys anywhere they are eager to get a bite out of it. Some of them even get severe attacks of religion, in an effort to please the parole board.

I had myself the vision of the carrot, dangling on the periphery of my consciousness, throughout my days at the Lazy L. Now I could safely excise that image from my mind. I would get no parole. So, it was a two year four month pill I forced down my throat that night of fitful sleep.

Yet when the morning came, on exercise, hands in jacket pockets, shoulders hunched in the time honoured deportment of prisoners, kicking at imaginary small stones, I was able to say to David, "Fuck 'em. It's costing them, what, a couple of hundred pounds a week to keep me here. So who are they hurting? Only themselves! The silly bastards."

David was tailormade company in which to express such views.

Because he had the leading role in so many Visiting Magistrate farces he had no more remission left to lose. He told me with matter of fact nonchalance that, in actual days, he had lived through seven years of a sentence which had started as a six year one. He had a few more months left to finish before his final release, and he expected to do the whole of that in the punishment block.

"Don't let the bastards grind you down," he said.

"Who me? Ha! Never," I replied. But inside, it hurt, terribly.

Chapter 23

As expected life in the punishment block at the Lazy L was not punishing, just laborious.

Linear time seemed to curl around like a snake trying to grab its own tail; so that after a few days one's ability to recall the chronology of daily events was lost into an indefinite past; it became very difficult after a while to say with certainty, whether so and so minor event, or conversation, had taken place the day before or the day before that.

It was a soporific routine that never varied: breakfast, bang up; half an hour's automation exercise, walking clockwise around the tiny yard. Throughout the whole time I was there, the nutter sang the first two lines of "That ole black magic," over and over again. In the end David and I didn't hear him.

After exercise, bang up; routine visits from officials of the prison, the governor or chief, welfare officer, priest, doctor, and anyone else whose duty it was to visit the punishment block once a day. These people usually stayed in the cell for micro seconds. The distance between us in that 8 ft square room was an enormous gulf; the ritual intonation next, 'morningeverythingallrightgood', and they were off before you could clear your throat, or say "nice weather we are having today."

The doctor especially was a man with a remarkable turn of speed at the door. Sometimes in his haste he even forgot the standard configuration; he appeared at the door peering over the shoulder of the screw who had opened the door, and then disappeared wordlessly. One just caught a glimpse of an alcoholically ruined face, strips of thin liver lips that parted in what may have been a sneer, or a smile, it was difficult to say; and then he was gone.

After the period of visits which in some ways was the most novel part of the day, monotonous routine took over, lunch, bang up, one hour in the gym—weights, badminton, or trying to get involved in David's most recent passion, Yoga,

At 4 pm the day was virtually over. What remained was, shower, bang up, evening meal, and at about 5 pm bang up for the night. The doors were opened again briefly at about 8 pm for a head count, and a mug of tea.

The locking and unlocking of doors in the punishment block was done manually; the electronic system only operated in the main prison.

So when the night screw jangled away down the corridor, the sound was the official announcement that another meaningless day in limbo had been marked up against your name.

As befits someone who was in the punishment block for smoking cannabis, it was also the go ahead signal to light up the peace pipe, constructed from silver foil supplied by David. It was also David who was able to lend me a piece of dope, fatefully the size of a pea with an understanding that I would return a similar amount to one of his friends in the main prison when I was allowed to re-enter normal prison life again. What the Visiting Magistrates would have done to me if I had been caught yet again, while I was in the punishment block, was a conjectural exercise I blanked out of my mind.

When I did leave the block it was in a fever of excited anticipation. It would be a treat to get back to the "freedom" of normal prison life I had become accustomed to.

The irony of that thought, that in one part of a prison, I could imagine that freedom was invested in another part of the same prison; that I looked forward to that short journey with such avidity; that the thought of playing my guitar, making myself a curry from leftovers, catching up on the gossip in Tiger Bay, participating in inter-wing badminton matches, that these comparatively mundane affairs should fill me with so much elation, was not lost on me even when it was happening. I was the village kid going to the big town to see the exotic sideshows he knew would be there.

Literally ten metres away, connected by two sets of double doors, the main prison spread out into the wings where the residents lived. Yet the difference in the social temperature at the end of those ten metres was what managed to spell that most abstruse of words: freedom. Just the ability to divert myself in more ways than I had been allowed to in the punishment block, spelled that word for me.

Waiting impatiently for the doors to be opened, to partake of those pleasures, I speculated that the definition of certain words had been revised or illuminated for me by the prison experience. Freedom was one such word.

It had once lived quite complacently in my vocabulary of abstract words; from time to time I would take it out, and pronounce it upon my circle of acquaintances in grandiose references to politics or communal conditions. I took it for granted, that it was self evident, that I myself had always been free.

When the men came to my home that day and said, "You are under arrest," and all the events unfolded that were to turn my life upside down, inside out, and I eventually found myself in prison doing a ten year sentence, I further took it for granted that I had lost my freedom.

And I was right.

And I was so very wrong.

The standard definition of freedom that I recognized most easily was that it is 'the power or liberty to order one's own actions'. That, it seemed I had lost when I was put in prison; but it was only a partial loss. There were new conditions, other compensations, within that loss that kept the word alive. I was given the time and the opportunity to learn a new language; the idiom of Spanish when it started to take root offered me glimpses of a horizon I did not know existed. And I would never have known how entrancing that vista was, if I had not made the effort—an effort that was made almost obligatory by the regime of prison life.

My body, like an untended garden, neglected for fifteen years, was cleaned up, weeds of fat destroyed, metabolism restored to a point where I used to sometimes feel a sort of euphoria of physical wellbeing. Badminton, a game I once used to think was for poofs and pansies, became an intensely, highly demanding pastime that had me jogging, and jigging, with anticipation waiting to play.

Unbelievably, to anyone who had known me outside, I learned to cook, and to cook inventively enough with scraps of odds and ends, to have certain larcenous citizens of Tiger Bay covertly watching my every move in the kitchen, in order to steal one of my original recipes.

I discovered also after two years of impassioned assault on my guitar, and my neighbours' eardrums, that musically I had no talent; but within that discovery there were rare moments of reward. Anyway, it kept me interested and occupied for hundreds of hours.

Lastly, it was in those long lonesome prison periods of time called 'bang up' that I began to toy and tinker with a writing skill whose end result is this book.

All these opportunities were offered to me in prison. In time these activities became the highlights of my life; I looked forward to the time of their happening with eagerness. There were hours and whole days when I was completely happy. Yet, in a conventional sense I had lost my freedom. I should have been unhappy and desolate, on my knees in misery, begging to go out to taste freedom again.

The concept I had believed was as neatly, and simply, packaged as a banana, was not like that at all; it was more like a tightly wound cabbage, one leaf under another; each one a layer of relative freedom. There are no outermost, or innermost, leaves to this cabbage; its numbers are proportionate to the number of personalities in the world. It goes on indefinitely. One man's holiday of fun, might be another man's station of suffering. The components of anguish or exultation are unpredictable. I knew this for myself, the understanding slowly crystallized in me that there had been times in so-called prison when I had felt more free than at other times in the outside world of so called freedom. When the men said, "You are under arrest," they set in motion the mechanism to unroll another leaf. Further, when the other men in the prison had said, "You're going down the block," another layer disappeared. The power of liberty to order one's own actions were more limited. In time, telling fanciful stories to David about my plans for the future, and twisting my body into Yoga shapes would have become the new highlights of my life.

Chapter 24

As soon as I left the punishment block I forgot of its existence. Nothing happened while I was there that was so extraordinary as to leave any significant traces on my memory. It had been a dull, featureless time of existence, easily forgotten. Yet, two years after my release, beginning in a Chelsea cafe, that time in the punishment block at the Lazy L has jumped in from the margin of memory to demand more reflection.

It would be dramatically apposite to act the prophet and say that I sensed the subsequent drama and disaster that was to attend David's life, while I was there in his presence, but it was not so.

He was one of a type I had met in prison several times. Usually, they had been given exemplary sentences for something minor, (in David's case it was passing counterfeit travellers cheques) and who had never accepted that their sentences had been justified. In the prison climate, dedicated to being as troublesome as possible, they grew enormous chips. Chips that weighed so heavily on their shoulders, that they had no chance of keeping their balance in society ever again. Their communities created them; prison was their finishing school.

The 'soft' crimes they had committed in the past was for softies. In prison they had met real gangsters, and hardmen; and had recognized that what their instincts had suggested, prison had confirmed.

It was going to be guns and grenades next time.

And so it was for David. In the late summer of 1982 I met him by chance having coffee at the Chelsea Kitchen in the King's Road. His outsize nose (subject of many prison nicknames) and shoulder length, carefully groomed blond hair, made him recognizable despite the camouflage of civilian clothes.

My flat was just around the corner in Markham Street, and we went there to have a joint. He was wearing casual, but expensive brand-name clothes. In his right hand he carried a smart new brief case. He could have been a young executive in the electronics, or entertainment fields.

A brand new VW Golf convertible was parked on double yellow lines outside a bank, as though it had been placed there to attract as much attention as possible. He waved at it with lifted briefcase.

"Just bought it," he said.

I started to feel uneasy. I had been living a low profile, high profit, life in London for a few months, and I did not want any bright stars like David lighting up the vicinity around me. But it was too late, we were already in my apartment before I could think of any reasonable excuse why we should not go there.

My unease increased to anxiety when David took his jacket off. He was carrying a holstered gun under his arm. He did not refer to it, which was his way of telling me that it was common practice in his circles, to walk the streets of London with a gun under one's arm.

I made coffee, rolled a joint and began a stilted conversation. David was fidgeting like a hyperactive child, walking all around the room, looking out of the window, turning around suddenly, sitting down, getting up abruptly. His eyes were unnaturally mercurial, jumping from one object to another with sharp switching motions of his head. His engine was racing at high speed on some rare fuel, and I did not want to be anywhere near sucking distance of that slipstream.

During the conversation, in one of his restive movements, he flipped the briefcase open. There were two handguns in there of differing sizes, and packets of currency notes, the way it comes from the bank, encased in cellophane. I estimated there was about five thousand pounds in tens and twenties.

"I got a couple of these for sale. Know anyone wants one? Ammo' as well," he said.

It was like asking the Dalai Lama the way to the best brothel in town.

My anxiety turned into high-level paranoia. I just wanted to end the meeting then and there and get him out of my apartment.

I shook my head vigorously and made fluttering negative movements with my hands. I felt compromised just by having that briefcase and David in my flat. I didn't ask him where he had got the guns or money from, and changed the subject. The phone rang; it was a tennis companion confirming a proposed game. After he had rung off, I spoke imaginatively into the dead line, that yes, I did realise how serious it was, and that I would meet him in the same place under the third lampost, in fifteen minutes and hung up. I apologised to David and said we would have to leave right away, as the third lampost reference was a code for Red Alert in my circles. I made out it was an extreme emergency that I had to attend to. For a second his glittering amphetamine eyes calmed down, became wary, and I knew what he was thinking. Momentarily he was worried about being dragged into *my* slip stream.

On the street I ascertained which way David was going, and practically ran away in the opposite direction. I did not want to meet him again, in that condition.

In fact, I never met him again, in any condition. Two weeks later David was arrested for armed robbery, during the course of which a policeman had been shot in the leg. It was a serious charge; a number of guns and ammunition had been recovered from him, and there were other equally serious charges to follow. In these circumstances the prisoner in question is held by the police, and prison service, in extra secure conditions. They lavish care and attention on him. He is their special prize to be taken to Court in good condition.

On Christmas Eve 1982 David advanced from the inside pages of the newspapers into front page headline status. He had escaped from Marlborough Street Court Police Station. He was a gift from the deities of journalism to sub editors: 'Houdini escapes', 'Dave the Rave on the loose again', this time with innumerable photographs of him, in some of which he was dressed as a woman carrying a handbag, in which it was alleged, there had been a loaded pistol. Official statements from the police boosted his notoriety: 'This man is vicious and dangerous, do not approach him', they warned.

Suddenly for a few days David Martin was a very sought-after man. Someone like that, basically a loner, who creates a big splash on the media is an embarrassment to both sides. The Law wants him back, because while he is free they are made to look inadequate. The organized villains, unlawfully minding their own businesses, also want the law to get him back, because while he is loose their places of business are being raided in the general hunt for David. Such a person acts as a catalyst who agitates the sediment of a big city where illegal but tolerated activities flourish. It is in the interests of the unlicensed gambling house, or massage parlour, or out of hours boozer, to see that he is back behind bars. Friends were at a premium for David.

Then the public got into the act. They sighted him here, and they sighted him there; dressed as a Buddhist monk in Glasgow, and disguised as a bus conductress in Clapham South. By and large the tabloid reading populace *want* to believe in a monster on the loose. It's good entertainment.

The police came right back with another statement: 'Exactly as we said. This man is not only dangerous, and cunning, now you have seen that he is also a master of masquerade, and false appearances.

Although we are completely outnumbered and temporarily outwitted by him, we shall press on. In the meantime, what you good people could do is to write a few letters to the press in support of our thirteen and a half percent wage claim.'

More bizarre photographs were issued of David dressed as a woman in a black sleeveless evening gown, and another artist's impression of what he would look like with short dark hair, and wearing glasses. But nothing can lessen that enormous nose; he carried it like a cross in the middle of his face. This kind of hype is not only persuasive propaganda for the public, fed on sensational imagery by the media, it is also invigorating medicine for the young detectives assigned to hunt him down. It keeps them on their toes.

They were promised action when they joined the force; now they have it; at last they have a chance to use guns. Rabid dog on the loose! Licence to kill! Clint Eastwood in Magnum Force! Starsky and Hutch! Incendiary words to implant in young men who have just missed the Great Falklands War.

Elements of farce attended the chase. Another man called David Martin, a shoe salesman from Scunthorpe, was attending a shoe conference with his boss's wife on company business. After a hard day demonstrating shoes, he was just about to show the lady a special technique he had with his shoehorn, as conscientious shoe salesmen should, when two policemen rolled out from under the very bed that the demonstration was taking place on, and arrested him—at gunpoint.

The next incident was a more publicly played drama.

It is reasonable to suppose that as in any hunt the element of competition was strong in the hunters, especially with all the bullshit they have been given about David's prowess in gun fights. His record to date of having, in a moment of panic, shot a policeman in one leg is amplified, embellished, until he is accepted as a real life Rambo, who can only be stopped with bazookas and bombs. They all want to be first, to have the honour, and prestige, of being in on the kill.

And kill it very nearly was. A group of them, nervously hair triggered, followed David's girlfriend, and observed with their trained policeman's eyes that she and two other men picked David up in a Mini. They followed the car down Kensington High Street when the evening traffic was at its densest. The lads were unable to contain themselves any longer; as the lights held up the traffic, they got out of their car and approached the Mini with drawn guns, in the style and demeanour sanctioned by their television heroes. They poked their guns into the back of the Mini, and with all their hours of marksmanship coming to fruition in one grand triumphant moment, they shot the man sitting next to the girl, with unerring aim, from a distance of eighteen inches. Naturally enough, they missed a couple of times, so they fired several shots to be sure.

At this point it seems their television role playing faltered somewhat; eye witness reports say they hugged each other, and were giggling hysterically. This is quite legitimate behaviour in team sports; it is customary to passionately embrace the goal scorer, or if he has done exceptionally well to discreetly gang-bang him behind the goal posts. And that is all the boys were doing, congratulating each other for having won the contest against David Martin, especially with such a fine score: Police Officers 7, David Martin nil. In fact, as the post-mortem of the competition showed, David did not have a chance of scoring; he didn't have a gun. And he wasn't David!

The girl was screaming. One of the boys hauled the inert bleeding body out of the car, and gave it a clump on each ear with the butt of his pistol. It was an exuberant after-match gesture, but the girl seemed not to have got into the spirit of the event. She screamed even louder, making violent dissenting movements with her body. Seeing through a haze of adrenalin vapour, the policemen realised that she was not just screaming for the sound effect; she was trying to say something

And what she was mouthing had the shape of something awful. An intuition warned them that in these grim circumstances she would not, could not, be lying or trying to mislead them. The words they were most easily able to decipher, "Wrong man, wrong man."

By now all the television role playing had been totally abandoned; it was panic stations.

Suddenly the hunters see their own lives in headline flashes; they see their own trials, manslaughter, dismissal from the force; they see the rolling heads of their superior officers who deemed them old enough, and responsible enough, to carry guns.

The man who had so sportively pistol-whipped the body on the pavement now examines the contused face with great reverence, and dread anticipation, praying to the patron saint of policemen: that what he sees may give him the licence to clump it a couple of more times. But it is not to be. The girl is right. They have shot the wrong man.

One part of the police prayers was answered. The man in question, Peter Waldroff, did not die. A few months later with a haste that implied unconditional culpability, he was paid a quarter of a million pounds for his injuries.

Soon after the shooting fiasco all the loyalty David had reckoned on in friends, and lovers, had evaporated. The heat was too hot. He was set up by someone he trusted, and was captured after a short chase down an underground train tunnel.

At his trial the newspapers reported how impressed the courtroom had been with his demonstration of the mechanism of a certain type of handgun while giving evidence from the witness box. The man most impressed by it was the judge. When it was his turn to have a say, he showed how impressed he had been; he gave David twenty five years.

In the early part of 1983 David Martin hanged himself in Parkhurst prison on the Isle of Wight.

No doubt psychologists and social workers somewhere will debate and examine what produced the phenomenon, part Billy the Kid, part Boy George, that was David Martin. On one point they could not convince me otherwise. I saw it in the making.

The corpse that hung from the cell bars in Parkhurst Prison had a 'Made in HM Prison' label stamped on its forehead.

Chapter 25

Usually the gymnasium of any high security, long-term prison, acts as an amplifier that gathers up the sound in the rest of the prison and turns it into opinions of dissent, or approval. It is also a place, if one uses it regularly, and is on familiar terms with the people who work there, both screws and cons, to glean bits of intelligence, foreknowledge, of modifications to the prison regime. Generally speaking, it is a good listening post for both sides. It was there that we first heard that someone important, an adjective interchangeable with notorious, in prison terms, was being transferred to the Lazy L. Prisoners, each with his own 'absolutely reliable official' source of information turned it into a guessing game. Some said it was the Kray twins who were coming. Others said it was Charlie Richardson.

It's none of those, another said; two cells are being knocked into one in the punishment block to make a special unit for one man. When he does get here, no one will ever see him. He is being kept underground, for the rest of his life. If that were true, it amounted to a prison, within a prison, within a prison. Now who could warrant that sort of treatment? Only one man: Ian Brady, the unspeakable torturer and killer of children. If this man had not been put in prison for life, he would have been lynched by the people in his community, in whom he evoked such horror. If he had not been put in a prison, within a prison, other prisoners would have lynched him, in whom he evoked such horror. If he had not been put in a prison, within a prison, within a prison, other prisoners who had been put in a prison within a prison, would have lynched him, in whom he evoked such horror.

But the atmosphere in the gym, belied that possibility. Whoever was coming was well liked. Once or twice I overheard bits of a conversation between the gym PO and one of the orderlies; they were both laughing and joking, as though they had known the new arrival from another time, and another place.

Then one day after I had soundly whopped Ronnie Darke the gym orderly at Padda-Tennis, he showed his pique.

"Make the most of it while you can," he said. "In a few days there will be someone here, who will have you over at this game. You won't be able to play your little tricks with him."

I became personally interested then. Ever since I had first started using the gym at the Lazy L, the dormant skills, learned at school and college, playing proper tennis, had started to come back, and I was the acknowledged champion of Padda-Tennis in the prison. The game of Padda-Tennis may be described briefly as follows: wooden bat, as in ping pong but larger, tennis ball, low net, badminton court, under-arm service. The scoring system is as in tennis. All forms of gamesmanship, especially during matches, are not just permissible, they are obligatory.

We had a ladder of proficiency in the gym. I was Number One; the other ranks followed after that. It became part of the banter there; to address each other by our appropriate numeral. Inevitably, there was a touch of sarcasm about the way these numbers were used.

Naturally, as Number One I took my position seriously, constantly adjusting my crown and polishing it, making sure no one sneaked up behind me to snatch it away. Once a month we had a series of matches to decide the ranking for the next month. So far I had held on to the Number One title.

So when Ronnie Darke said there was someone coming to the Lazy L who was going to lift my crown, I started to work it out for myself.

There was a pertinent fact, buzzing around my head like a fly about to land. It was something I had read, or been told about. Then abruptly, it came to me, and other supportive clues made me certain.

Years earlier, before I had ever dreamt that I would one day go to prison myself, I had read a serialized version of a book by John Mc-Vicar in a Sunday paper. In it he had described how the half dozen prisoners held in a special unit of Durham prison had learned to play tennis, on a court they had built themselves. Since racquet sports had always been my preference, that fact had stuck in my mind, when other more interesting details of his book had been forgotten. I also knew through prison gossip, that when Ronnie Darke had been interested in banks, especially in the withdrawal counters of such institutions, John McVicar had been one of his associates.

Being reasonably conversant with prison arithmetic, I put two and two together, made a total of seven, and proceeded to tell everyone I knew, that the person being moved to the Lazy L was Mc-Vicar. I let it be understood that it was the Governor himself who had passed this information on to me. In the event, I was proved right, which enhanced my spurious reputation as a man with access to inside information.

Personal misfortune had brought me to prison; there, a small piece of information I had acquired years ago about another man's aptitude for playing tennis, and the fact that I remembered it, had become momentarily significant.

It validated for me the often expressed axiom of life that no one knows with certainty what tomorrow holds, or how the insignificant episodes of the present, might shape or influence the future.

If anyone had told me ten years earlier, that one day I would be hitching up my ragged prison shorts, metaphorically squaring my shoulders, and looking forward to the day when I could play Padda-Tennis against the legendary John McVicar whom the police had once titled, "'The most dangerous man in Britain', I would have laughed at such a preposterous notion. If ten years earlier, someone had told John McVicar that he would one day meet an Indian in prison, who would dazzle him with his footwork, destroy him with searing drives, frustrate him with whispering stop volleys, and confound him with his artistry, at the game of Padda-Tennis; perhaps he too would have laughed at such a preposterous notion.

In fact it was a few weeks before I met John, and a few weeks after that, before we played Padda-Tennis. There were two reasons for this.

The first was that it was the football season; it was played five-a-side in the gym, and with the regulation number on the fields outside. While the football mania gripped the residents of the lazy L, all other sports were temporarily shelved until their passion subsided.

The Lazy L football team was unusual. It was the only one in the league that was forced to play all its matches at home, by special order of the Home Office. It was thought that its members might make their way to other destinations during, or after the match, if they were allowed to play away games. The fact that they played at home was usually not a help to the team, as the spectators who were collectively doing hundreds of years of imprisonment between them, also by decree of the Home Office, were extremely derisory of their team.

I once saw our goal keeper, an Irishman of uncertain temperament, abandon his post, pull up the corner flag, and lay about him full strength behind the goal posts. He finished his display by hurling the corner flag like a javelin at an escaping member of his wrath; the ones he had attended to behind the goal posts were lying around in various degrees of shock. The goal keeper wasn't very popular with the team either; while he was out and about on his own business, the fullback had tried a stylish back pass which, egged on by the roars of the assembled spectators, slowly dribbled into the vacant goal mouth. When the goal keeper got back, the fullback had a mouthful of scathing words for him. Another punch-up ensued; dozens of uniformed men came running on to the pitch, and the game was abandoned. When last seen the goal keeper was being marched towards the punishment block, phalanxed by screws, but still managing to sing, 'We are the Champions', at the top of his voice. It was generally agreed that he had more of a future as a singer than as a goal keeper.

The other reason why I was not using the gym as much as I used to was because I was struggling through a personal crisis.

Up to that time, I had avoided serious violence in prison. Usually, diplomacy and compromises managed to avert any showdowns. Once or twice I had thrown a punch or two instinctively, and received a few back of the same quality. They were nothing to speak of, and were forgotten the next day.

But I had seen quite a lot of premeditated violence in prison; mostly the protagonists were prisoners, the other kind did not normally have observers. I had seen prisoners cut, stab, scald, boil, and bludgeon one another, but blithely assumed it could never happen to me. It did, without warning.

About three months earlier I had been singled out by the accounting department of a bookmaker's firm, run by a couple of London gentlemen. According to their ledgers, I owed them 50p. I said I did not. They said I did, more forcefully. I said I did not, more forcefully.

These exchanges, I treated in much the same way as I would have done demand notices from commercial enterprises in the world outside. That is to say, I ignored the first two requests. Then when their attitude started to harden, I asked to see photocopies of invoices, and other documents to ascertain my debt.

They came back with, "Don't get slippery with us. You lost it last week when you bet John Lloyd to beat Bjorn Borg at Wimbledon."

Now, that was a direct insult to me who professed to be knowledgeable about the game of tennis. I would not have bet on John Lloyd to beat Bjorn Borg's grandmother under any conditions. I told them that. They were not convinced. In any case, I pointed out, I could not with the best will in the world pay them any money just then as I was broke.

Then Barry's foam rubber boxes began to arrive and I was rich. I could have paid them without any hardship, but by then all communications between us had ceased; we were not speaking.

I heard through professional agitators on the wing, that they had referred to me as "That slimy Paki cunt who is going to get done soon". At this point, that most incendiary of human baggage, *face*, got in the way. I was definitely not going to pay them anything after I had heard that.

Face is a popular religion in long term prisons; for some men it is all they have left. Guided by that Oracle they lose all sense of reason and proportion. So, when the Oracle whispered in my ear that if I paid them the 50p I would become "That slimy Paki cunt", and be thought of as a coward as well, I listened.

I should have had the good sense to go to them and say, "Look, you think I owe you 50p. I don't think so. Let's settle it by tossing a coin." I believe they would have accepted that, as before that incident I had got on quite well with them.

But I did nothing, just waited for the first move from them. A few weeks went by— nothing happened. We were still not talking, but the bad feeling between us seemed to have lessened.

Naturally, with my newly acquired wealth I had several newly acquired friends. Fine upstanding fellows they were too; they said I should not worry about trouble from a couple of two-bit London gangsters. They gave me to understand that they would stick with me to the bitter end if there was any harassment from a London 'firm'. I felt confident and safe with such staunch comrades around me; popularity has a way of breeding a sense of inviolability.

So it was that one afternoon I ambled up the the third floor (the threes) to have a look at a painting that someone wanted to sell. My mind was oblivious to any danger, preoccupied with some small problem of the day. Violence was not in my thoughts at all.

From the periphery of my vision a figure got up from the screws table on the landing, where some prisoners were playing cards. He had been at the Lazy L for about a year. Although still in his early twenties he had a ponderous, hulking figure, like a heavyweight boxer gone to fat. His brain however was very lightweight, and if C wing had been a small village, his status in it would have been village lout. As he approached me I had no misgiving; a day or so earlier I had lent him some rice. I had no quarrel with this man.

I may have turned towards him, still completely relaxed, thinking he was going to say something about the rice he had borrowed. When he was within touching distance of me, without notice or preamble, he threw a clubbing right hand at me.

My next moment of consciousness was not pleasant. I seemed to have fallen down a well and was lying on my back looking up at a ring of indistinct faces. As wakenings go it was one of the worst of my life. I did not know what was going on.

My head felt sort of waterlogged. The faces were coming and

going, in and out of focus. An instinct warned me that I was in deep trouble. At first I thought I was drowning, and that the next time I saw the faces again in close up I should grab hold of one of them and take a deep breath. I never found out if I actually tried to do that or not, but I remember thinking that I should.

When the faces next came back into focus, they stayed that way, and reality was re-established. I was lying on a bed in the prison hospital. Other patients from adjoining beds were standing around looking down at me.

My first thought was one of utter relief that I wasn't down the well, or other deep hole, I thought I had fallen into. But I had no understanding of how I had got into hospital. I felt dazed, hypnotized; the idea passed through my mind that I had just had an operation and was coming round from the effects of an anaesthetic, and that the jumble of disjointed thoughts would clear up in a minute.

As a diagnosis of my condition it was pretty accurate, although the operation, and the surgeon, had both come as a surprise.

One of the faces belonged to a man I knew quite well. "What's going on?" I asked.

"Don't you know?" he looked surprised.

I tried to think, but a fuzzy inability to concentrate on any one thing prevented me from doing so. I shook my head.

"You've been in a fight," he said. I realised that my face and ribs were hurting.

"With whom?" I asked, but even before he replied the answer started to trickle through of its own accord. I saw again Lout's swinging right hand; it must have been the last conscious image my memory had retained.

This happened on a Friday. I was kept in hospital over the weekend; the doctor would see me on Monday morning to see if I was well enough to go back to the wing.

In those two days I was able to piece together what had happened. It was fairly simple.

Lout came from one of the lesser suburbs of London. His idols were London gangsters from the inner city. The prestige of being known to be associated with them was his greatest ambition in life. When a couple of them suggested that if he 'did the slimy Paki cunt' on C wing he would be allowed to lick their boots, he couldn't wait to realise his dream.

He must have knocked me out with the first punch. Eye witnesses, too timid or unconcerned to intervene, told me later that when I was lying on the floor one of the London gangsters popped up from a nearby burrow to advise Lout how to proceed; how many punches to the head, how many to the ribs, and how many kicks to the kidneys he should administer. Since I was serenely unconscious, I had no objections.

There was a glaring discrepancy in the end result of this assault that I have never properly understood. It was an inconsistency for which I was extremely thankful. Having knocked me out with a tremendous, roundhouse first punch, and being given the opportunity to use me as an inert punch bag, to punch and kick for several minutes without interference or opposition, he was somehow not able to inflict any further damage that was commensurate with that first blow which had felled me. My ribs hurt for a couple of days but nothing was broken. The left side of my face was swollen, and eating was painful, but even that only lasted a few days. One reporter of the event, with the characteristic relish that one reserves for the recital of another's catastrophe, told me that as Lout kept hitting me in the face and body I was making a snoring, gurgling sound, and he thought I was dying.

This man had excellent credentials to describe the sound dying men make, as he was doing a life sentence for sending a couple of people on their way to the other world.

The only plausible explanation for how I had survived the incident so well was paradoxically to do with his size. A ponderous physical type nearly sixteen stone, and six foot two inches tall would have a weight distribution and leverage problem to deliver his punches with optimum effect, while kneeling down; it would be a little like trying to box on one's knees. The other factor that may have helped me was that since my head was resting on the floor, a good deal of the impact of his blows was absorbed by the ground. If Lout had lifted my head off the floor each time he punched me, I guess he would have killed me. His lack of expertise probably saved my life. With a brain he would have been a highly dangerous man.

Over the weekend The Chief came to see me. I thought he was going to ask for behind the scene details of what had happened. Why it had happened, who was involved and so on. I had already prepared a, "I didn't see anything, it's all a mystery to me," answer. I need not have bothered. He didn't ask any questions.

He said he already knew all there was to know. Then he gave me a simple warning. Certain changes had been made, but I was being sent back to C Wing. It was to be a probationary period for me. If I tried to mount an assault of my own against those who had assaulted me, I would be shanghaid out of the Lazy L pronto. There were only two areas of convict life on which he took a tough line he said: gang violence and trying to escape. So far I had not tried my hand at either. Don't start anything now.

It was a clear and direct caution from a man I respected.

"Any way," he said as he was leaving, "do what you bloody well like in two months' time."

Then explaining, he continued, "I'm a Hampshire boy like yourself and I'm going back to retire there, as The Chief at Winchester. Do yourself a favour. Use your loaf. I've done my time. Now do yours, and get back to the Isle of Wight to your family, and never come back to these places again."

It was sound advice. It had completely left my head by the time I got back to C wing. I wanted revenge. The first strike had been made, but I was still alive, still standing. I was held in thrall by one of the most powerful impulses in human history; the will to avenge oneself; to have a return match; to get even; to sustain my pride.

Since the opposition was a 'firm', this was going to be gang violence, not personal combat. To fight battles one needs troops.

Troops? Where are you, troops? Can you hear me, troops?

This is your general calling. I looked in every crevice and corridor of C wing for the loyal band of men who had promised to help me if there was any trouble from a London gang. I could not find one who was prepared to back his words with action.

Two of them told me quite candidly that they wished to forget what they had said, and further, to forget they had ever known me.

Another one said, why yes, he remembered saying he would help me but that was last week, before he had become a devout Buddhist. He implored me to join him in prayer to find perfect enlightenment. I told him I would like to do that later, but first I had some urgent blood to spill.

Two others avoided me with such diligence that I understood what their absence was saying.

The changes The Chief had spoken of were arbitrary; they made no significant difference to the state of affairs. The Londoners and Lout had been moved on to different wings so as to break up the gang, but it was still possible to come across them in the general communal areas of the Lazy L, like the gymnasium and cinema hall.

Two or three times Lout and I had come face to face in the gym. He had a confident smirk on his face, that made my blood bubble and froth. I was also frightened, but rage was the greater emotion. I worked my features into noncommittal indifference and walked on. But instinct was prompting me to run at him screaming with anger.

One of the beneficial effects of losing erstwhile friends was that my dope was lasting a lot longer, so money was not decreasing at such a rapid rate. I had plenty of both, so I imposed a siege mentality on myself.

A general with battle plans racing around his head and no troops to implement them tends to become morose and withdrawn. I started to stay in my cell in the evening and not use the gymnasium as much as I used to.

About a month later, when these plans were beginning to be moved over to the long-term-hopes-and-desires section of my mind I heard a whisper that made the matter first priority again.

It came from The Sheikh. Throughout my troubles with the Londoners he had remained neutral. He was a bookmaker himself and knew them quite well; it was obligatory that he did not take sides. He had even urged me once to pay them the 50p and be done with it. He even suggested that he would absorb it into one of his bookmaking adjustments with them, so that it would not look as if I had lost face. I had thanked him, but refused the offer.

After my return from hospital he had commiserated with me, but maintained the same neutral position. So although I could not look to him for practical help, I always trusted him.

Then news came to us on C wing that one of the Londoners who was an A* man had been shanghaid in the middle of the night. It was an adjunct of this news that The Sheikh was warning me about.

"Before he left," The Sheikh said, "he has been telling people that the reason he was moved was because you had put his name up as the person responsible for your accident. Be careful, my friend, I have heard they are planning further accidents for you. Cutting accidents."

He flicked his forefinger across his face.

The Sheikh's old fashioned cadences that hinted of law courts seemed to make the news more serious, more disturbing.

I felt very vulnerable. If they had recruited Lout to beat me up, a man I had no reason to be afraid of, who might they have got hold of this time? For the first time in prison I felt racially assailable. I started to wonder about the men on my wing, to try and predict who my next assailant might turn out to be.

I retreated further into my cell, like a snail backing into its shell. Going to the gym became a clandestine operation; usually I went

---

* Prisoner in a high security prison deemed to require extra attention.

without advertising the fact, so that no reception committees could be prearranged for me. I charted a map of the Lazy L in my head of safe and unsafe places to be. Corridors that I had walked for years had to be reassessed for ambush points. I stopped going to the once weekly cinema; it would have been a totally indefensible position sitting there in the dark.

I armed myself. A door hinge sharpened, and shaped, in the Light Engineers and wedged into a short piece of mop handle was tucked into my waist band. Its purpose was to cut, not stab. The sight of one's own blood leaving the body in large quantities dampens the fervour of most people to continue fighting. In my right pocket, always open, ready to use at an instant's notice was a more exotic weapon.

Necessity resurrects strange memories. This one went back to my boyhood. I once saw a man being dragged along to the police station by a big policeman in a bazaar in South India. The policeman was enjoying the situation, kicking and swearing at his quite passive prisoner. From the crowds a woman, tiny, compared to the policeman, walked up behind him and lightly brushed her hand across his face. The next moment the air was filled with crying policeman. He was howling in pain long after the woman and her man had escaped. I had been very impressed.

I found out the name of the magic wand that could transmute a belligerent policeman into a blubbering child.

Chilli powder.

It was commonplace enough among those of us who cooked for ourselves. I bought myself an ounce—not for cooking.

I started to practice different techniques of throwing the contents of a plastic bottle filled with sand at a face-sized piece of cardboard stuck to the back of my cell door. As a co-ordinated manual discipline it was like drawing a gun and firing it cowboy style. There was a problem. Sometimes this gun had the disconcerting tendency of going off in one's own face. But after a while, when I was about ankle deep in sand I became quite expert at it. It was, as in any sport, a question of timing.

Here are a few basic rules and postures for anyone wishing to learn the art of chilli-powder throwing.

Make sure the bottle is open and held loosely in your fist, so that the top is covered by your palm. Rest that fist nonchalantly at the top end of your trouser pocket as though you have adopted a new style of walking. If you see anyone approach you who might be an adversary take your fist out of the pocket and casually swing it along as you walk. In the terminology of firearms one could say your gun is now cocked. If he is an enemy, and, he intends to cut you, he will have to get close enough. Wait till you see the whites of his eyes, then with a wristy movement, like dealing cards, flick the contents of the bottle in them. If a ten thousandth part of the bottle gets him in his eyes you may have a game of blindman's-buff with him. If a ten thousandth part of it gets in your own eyes you won't mind him cutting you up; the pain in your eyes will be far greater.

It was in this precarious condition, wavering between fear and excitement, that I first met John McVicar.

In a prison where weightlifting and body building were a fetish, and the sum total of years of grunting and groaning over heavy pieces of metal were strutting about the gym—even in such a place John was noticeable. Muscles bulged profusely everywhere. On closer examination one could see that his bone structure was of average size. He was about 5 foot 9 inches tall with close-cropped wiry hair; the epithet 'Big John' that I had heard used seemed misapplied, despite his muscularity.

The difficulty in forming an impression of a man with a reputation good or bad is that what one has heard gets in the way of an unbiased judgement.

McVicar is a legend in British prisons. As in all legends some of it is apocryphal no doubt, but many-faceted.

First there was his physical toughness. Jumping through plate glass windows and eating a couple of police dogs for breakfast were casual experiences for him—they said. When cornered, armies of policemen were needed to capture him—they said. Even when taken into custody there was no guarantee that he would remain in captivity for long, he could escape from anywhere—they said.

Even after the hyperbole had been stripped away, it left the picture of an extraordinarily enterprising and hard man.

Second there was his academic career. It is all too easy to accept an easy life in a long-term prison; a life without effort or reward; to let one inconsequential day follow another; to become emasculated by the institution. It is very difficult to stick to self-imposed disciplines in such places. Innumerable prisoners try. Only the very few succeed.

John was one of them. With an interminable sentence of twenty-six years to face, and realizing that his escaping days were over, he decided to study Sociology. He began at the beginning; O levels, A levels, BA. When I met him he was half way into an MA.

It is that combination of Academic and Action Man, that makes him unusual in any company, and particularly so in prison.

I tried to fit some of these stories to the genial man with the broken-toothed smile who was talking to me.

I had been playing an improvised and solitary game of Padda-Tennis against the wall in the gymnasium. My weaponry, bottle and blade, were lying a few feet away covered by a towel.

As soon as John saw what I was doing he came over grinning, as if he had recognized an old friend. His interest was obvious. He asked if it was played much at the Lazy L. I told him about the Padda-Tennis ladder we had, not forgetting to let him know that I was Number One.

"We'll see about that," he said. "Want a game tomorrow?"

I told him how the football season had temporarily suspended all other games.

"Never mind about all that," he said. You just be here in the morning. "I'll fix the rest with Malcolm."

What I did not know was that John had already got himself a job as an extra gym orderly, and his opinions on what could or could not be done in the gym were already being felt.

When I got there the next morning at the time allotted for cleaners John had already got the net up and was practising with one of the other orderlies.

"Right, now let's get this nonsense about who's Number One sorted out," he said, windmilling his arms energetically, and doing knee bends. If it was meant to intimidate me, it certainly did that. But it was also the sort of challenge with intimations of camaraderie that appealed to me.

We played three sets. Every one was close, but I held on to my Number One title. If strength, tenacity, and fitness were the only criteria he would have won by a mile. Fortunately for me, skill, courtcraft and consistency had the edge that day. Watching John race about the court snorting and grunting, his face set in a grimace of determination, taking enormous scything swings at the ball, I started to appreciate how that accumulation of brawn, and sinew, with a will to be free, could give policemen a terrible headache, as sometimes he had done—literally.

After the match John was still enthusiastic.

"Give you best this time," he said. "But I'll have some more of that tomorrow."

We played several times that week and under the influence of his keenness others joined. The once monthly challenge matches to decide rankings became weekly tests.

Padda-Tennis which had been flagging through lack of interest got a new boost. John had still not won a set off me, but he was pressing hard. He had established himself in No 3 position on the ladder behind Ronnie, and he was making ominous sounds from there. The ladder was now prominently displayed outside the gym office. The banter that involved using our rankings as nicknames began again.

One morning a few weeks later I was stopped at the gym door by John.

"Seen the board today have you, Number One?" he asked. He had a grin on his face as big as his biceps, which were very big. John's name was in Number Two slot right under mine.

"I'm so sharp now, I'm seeing the ball like a water melon. I'm gonna' destroy you next week," he said.

"One day a man may walk on Mars, Number Two" I said.

The following week when the ranking matches were played John fulfilled his threat. He beat me in straight sets. It was like light infantry against a tank. He just bulldozed past all my defences. For the first time he had used different tactics against me; there were no more long baseline rallies. He just whacked the ball as hard as he could and charged up to the net, flailing his arm and snarling menacingly. It worked. I couldn't seem to pass him down the sides, and lobbing was impossible as the roof was too low.

Since the game had first been started at the Lazy L I had always been Number One. I had become complacent imagining that if I just returned the ball over the net every time my opponents would make the mistakes, as invariably they did. I had not foreseen the possibility that someone would take the initiative and attack the way John had done.

I was shattered. To be beaten was bad enough; but to be beaten in straight sets with no game strategy for next time was far worse. It drove all thoughts of Lout and the Londoners out of my head. I was still aware that I was in physical danger, but, on that day it seemed to be of secondary importance to losing my Number One position.

It may be difficult out there on the outside to comprehend that, or to take it seriously. It is palpably true that when a person's circumstances are reduced; when the limit of his horizon has been foreshortened; when the compound of the prison is his whole world, and he has come to terms with these reductions in the quality of his life, then there is a proportionate lowering of his ambitions, desires and aspirations. His preoccupations and pastimes are also scaled down. But the complexity of his characteristics especially the dominant ones, the ones to do with so called machismo, ones like competitive rivalry, assertion of territorial rights, acquisition of power or property, the will to avenge oneself, one or more of which may have brought him to prison in the first place—these remain. They have to have outlets. That was why the Londoners enlisted Lout to beat me up over 50p; why I was prepared to blind them in return if I could. And why it nagged me like a toothache the day I lost at Padda-Tennis to John McVicar.

All those drives and forces within you that shaped your life out there are still with you in prison; it is just that the means of fulfilling them have changed.

The next morning I was in the gym early, impatient to have another game with John.

I hurried into the gym PO's office. John was reading a newspaper. "Come on matey, we're losing time," I said.

He looked up sharply. The smile of greeting on his face froze, his eyes turned stony. I had seen that look on his face once or twice before directed at someone who had overstepped the mark with him. It is not a pleasant experience to have John stare at you like that. Fortunately for me he was joking.

"Before you come in here calling me matey, go outside and look at the board, then come back in and rephrase your question."

I got the message, and did as he asked. When I came back in after wiping my feet on the door mat, I said, "Pardon me, Number One, for intruding into your current affairs study, but I was wondering, sir, if you would condescend to have a game of Padda-Tennis with a humble Number Two."

"Enough of the bollocks. Get the net up. You're wasting time standing there talking," he said.

That day he beat me again but this time in three sets. I was quite relieved, for in the losing I established that it was my backhand that was losing me most points; if I hit my returns low enough John could not bludgeon it past me from the net.

In the intervening period before the next ranking matches I started to practice again, an exercise I used to think was beneath me.

The following week on the day of the ranking matches John tried to get out of it on account of an Achilles tendon injury.

I advised him of Rule 3B, subsection F, of the International Federation Handbook on Padda-Tennis wherein it is stated that if a person refuses a challenge for whatever reason he automatically loses his placement to the challenger.

John limped on to the court grumbling and muttering. He limped right through the knock-up. When we started to play the match his limp miraculously left him and he was leaping about the court like a kangaroo.

I managed to win my title back that day. But from that time until he left the Lazy L there was no telling whose name was going to be in the number one slot on any given week. Just as I thought I had finally got the upper hand John would come back to disillusion me; just as he thought he had the answer I would come back to confound him.

So it went on through the summer of '78. The Great Christmas Padda-Tennis championships began. The tension and speculation were fantastic; that is to say, two people were wondering who was going to win. The rest of the world didn't really care one way or the other. You must understand that this tournament was the equivalent of making the final of Wimbledon outside. The stadium was packed with spectators. Seven of them. Four were doing weights and by the internal geography of the gym were forced to watch. The other three were two gym orderlies and a PEI who kept nipping off for cups of tea and biscuits while the players battled on.

It was big bad McVicar against clean-cut Krishnamma as anyone in the Padda-Tennis world could have predicted.

I won the first set easily and thought I was going to coast through. John won the next two and thought he was going to coast through. I won the fourth. The last set was going to decide the outcome of the match which had lasted over two hours.

I looked across the court and felt a tremendous admiration for my opponent. This scholar of the Social Sciences who could still say, 'I done' for 'I did' in the right company, and thereby proclaimed to the world where he had come from; this armed robber of violent action, and daring escapes, who could discuss learnedly some abstruse theory of sociometry in the right company, and thereby proclaimed to the world where he was going; a man separated from me by an enormous gulf of different formative experiences, whose fearsome reputation preceded him wherever he went, who was still affable and friendly to anyone who cared to respond.

I won the fifth set, and was almost sorry to do so; it had been such a great match.

The Queen and the Duchess of Kent were unable to award the prizes; an absent minded Malcolm handed me an envelope with the prize in it the next morning: two pounds in silver.

After the Christmas competition which was the highlight of the Padda-Tennis calendar, interest in the game waned. I accepted John's offer to join him in light workouts. as he termed them. They may have been light for him, for me they were extremely heavy.

First there were two hundred sit ups in batches of fifty. After that, on the point of collapse, physical resources all but drained, there was interval running to do; a cruel exercise which entailed running as fast as you could up and down the length of the gym (about 40 metres) ten times, resting for 60 seconds, then off again, five sets of those. I never did manage to finish the last one. John would sometimes do an extra five, just for fun. Then it was five one minute rounds on the speed-bag to loosen up. By the end of it I was ready to go to bed for a week.

In the days that spanned the old year and the new I got to know John at a different level. Beginning with our shared zest for a racquet sport, the conversation spilled into other areas of mutual interest: women, money, parole. In fact parole was an issue very much on John's mind at that time.

"What more do I have to do for them," he asked of us one day in the gym. "I've took degrees, I've writ a book, what more do the cunts want off me? Blood?"

I could only agree with him silently. Of the hundreds of men I had met who had spoken musingly about parole, John deserved it most. There was a man who was intelligent enough, practical enough, to know that his days as an armed robber, or for that matter a law breaker in any major way, were over.

"If I do get out," he once said, "and something big goes off, I'd be in the frame right away, wouldn't I? I'd be stupid to think anything else."

Meetings with John were restricted to the gym, and outside on the playing fields at weekends, as he was on a different wing. Getting to know him came in snatches of conversation here and there in the areas where the wings were allowed to intermingle; as such the depth of our relationship was not friendship in the truest evaluation of that term, but I knew him better than a casual acquaintance. Then one day John offered me his help in a way that returned a measure of my pride to me. I have been indebted to him for that ever since, for such as I am, pride and face were humps born on my back, and which I have carried with me as long as I can remember.

When I first met John he had already heard through gym gossip of my encounter with Lout. He offered me some vague all-purpose advice that I should stay with my own kind of people, and not mix with gangsters like that, who were in a different league to me. Beyond that we didn't speak about it, and the topic changed to other matters.

After the warning from The Sheikh I told no one of the armoury I had started to carry with me; the element of surprise would be my greatest asset. As the days went by and the opposition had not made any moves, my fears were being allayed; precisely the complacent attitude that had made the last incident possible. The chilli-powder was getting lumpy, like salt exposed to air, and I had to pulverize it every few days. I dreaded having to use it, and dreaded even more not carrying it with me. It was an apprehensive, jittery time for me.

After the Christmas competition, a day came when I was in the small back room of the gym, lying on a plastic mat that stank of other men's sweat, doing sit ups, counting laboriously, cheating occasionally. It was a dingy, depressing room, closed in like a public lavatory, where the walls echoed the twilight dreams of men diseased by hopelessness, a sweaty, sordid, ill-lit room that gave me bad vibes, and which I was always glad to be out of as soon as possible.

John was ferociously thumping the heavy punchbag a few feet away, making grunting sounds of satisfaction as he landed heavy lefts and rights. I was trying to synchronize the sit ups to the swings of the bag as it rocked and heaved like a small boat on its mooring. It was an attempt to imbue some variety into a boring, but strenuous exercise.

There was a sound behind my back from the open door; imagination took flight like a frightened bird and translated the noise into someone shifting his weight from one foot on to another, as though he was about to launch himself, or something at me. It had to be Lout.

I took off from the mat as though I had been stung on the bum by a bee, mouthing incoherent words of terror. My towel was at the foot the mat, and I dived towards it, uncoordinated, like a broken winged bird and at the same time contrived to look behind me to see who was there.

It was a cleaner who had just put his mop bucket down and was rolling a cigarette.

John had stopped abruptly, and was looking at me quizzically. "Whatsa matter?" he asked. "I thought you were having a heart attack."

I was out of breath with the situps, and the near miss I thought I had just had; it took a minute of jumbled explanation before John understood what I was saying. It produced a look of annoyance on his face.

"You still worried about those wallies, are you?" he asked. I explained about the most recent rumour about the cutting party planned for me. The frown on his face deepened, turned his face into a stony mask.

"So what's that you got there?"

I was still fumbling with the chilli-powder. I described to John what I intended to do with it.

He sniggered politely.

"Throw that rubbish away," he said. "You want something heavy in your hands if you're going to start anything with that lot."

"I wouldn't know how to use anything heavy," I said.

"Then come and see me," he replied. "I know how to handle them."

He started to punch the bag again, this time as though it was a mortal enemy. He started to speak, punctuating them with blows to the bag.

Left hook, "I've heard," right cross, "enough of this," straight left, "silly nonsense," round house right. "I'll give," left upper cut, "you a hand," head butt, "put a," elbow smash, "stop to it."

He finished with a huge kick at the bag that would have castrated an elephant.

It was my turn to take a few seconds to digest the import of his words.

"We'll go and pull 'em in the lunch break," he said.

"What if they don't, you know, listen?" I made a vague gesture of rejection.

"Then we'll do 'em," John said. "That's what you want isn't it?"

I didn't answer; suddenly I wasn't sure if that was what I wanted.

"Anyway, think about it," John said. "If you want to do it, I'll give you a hand. In the meantime I'm going to put it about that I'm involved in this thing now. We'll see what effect that has."

As we were leaving the gym that morning John asked me if the reason I wasn't coming to the Saturday films was because of the trouble. I told him it was.

"You come next week and sit with us," he said. "If anything starts up I'll be right there next to you."

Can you imagine the feelings of a general who had lost his army of toy soldiers to fortuitously have them replaced by a real live giant, the toughest, most formidable ally one could wish for. If power corrupts, it also sometimes imports a sense of responsibility. John could take care of Lout and the Londoners single-handed; by that I mean with one hand tied behind his back. It would be like using a sledgehammer to crush a row of cockroaches. Good generals could not contemplate such a wasteful manoeuvre. I felt the shadows of accountability gathering around me. I could not have cared less for what happened to Lout and company; my concern was for John.

He was waiting for an answer from the parole board on his fourth application. The fact that he had been transferred to the Lazy L from the extra secure special unit where he had been held for the past twelve years was a smoke signal from the chiefs of the Home Office that they viewed his case favourably. A discreet profile was what was expected of John at this stage. It was not the time when an act of violence was going to help his case; and if Lout or one of the others got hurt seriously, which was always possible, there would be no parole.

Then there was the real reason for my reluctance. For all my thoughts of blinding and cutting other human beings, acts of violence were always contrived at some cost; they did not come naturally. Remembrance of times when I had caused bodily harm to someone had churned like nausea inside me. Revenge has always been a fruit that tasted fine in my mouth, but turned sour in my stomach. And my acts of violence were small ones committed in moments when self control was lost. If ever I hurt someone seriously, having coldly planned the event, as I wished to hurt Lout, the memory of what I had done would revisit my conscience, to leave it heavy and swollen with regret that I had not chosen some other way. There should be some device in the natural order of creation that precludes people with pacifist tendencies from carrying the burden of face in their personalities. Now, I simply wanted an end to the whole stupid affair, and to forgo the taste of the fruit.

With John's help I saw how it might be possible to retain a portion of that precious cargo and to make peace at the same time. I decided to wait and see if John's announced presence in the dispute would be the neutralizing agent. I did not have to wait long.

The following Saturday the film was reputed to be ultra-violent, lots of blood and brains spilling out everywhere. Naturally, the hall was filled to capacity. I searched the audience for two pertinent groups. John and a couple of his friends were sitting at the back. Lout and Company were sitting a few rows in front. I threaded my way through the crowded chairs past Lout, who seemed a little disconcerted to see me there, to where John was sitting. He had kept a spare chair for me and I sat down feeling like the proverbial traveller who finds safe haven for the night. My feeling of safety grew as John included me in the conversation with others around him as if to demonstrate that I was part of their group.

One of the residual effects of mixing in star company is that one starts to act like one. I swaggered back to the wing, mixing with the throng where a sneak attack was conceivable, totally oblivious of danger. I had to restrain myself from patting the heads of passing convicts, and asking them if they wanted my autograph. I reached my wing without incident, and from that time the threat of Lout and company faded out of my mind.

Two or three days later, a peace pact of sorts was concluded on the football fields. The one remaining gangster came over to me accompanied by The Sheikh. He came to disassociate himself with all that had happened, saying it was the other fellow's idea all along to enlist Lout to do the beating up, and that he only heard about it after it had happened, and when he did he was overcome by grief etc. etc. I said, yes, of course, that must have been how it was, and then asked where that left Lout. Lout he said was on offer as a chopping block to be attacked and mutilated at will if I wished to do so, and nobody would help him. He indicated, that he, personally, was sick and tired of Lout's presence around him and would appreciate it if someone would arrange a hospital bed for him. In the hierarchy of armies Lout had achieved the lowest most expendable rank: cannon fodder.

The tables were turned. Lout was not to be seen in those public places where I walked jauntily, whistling. He stopped coming to the Saturday film, and was seen less in the gymnasium.

Two months later he got parole and left the Lazy L. A few months after that John was missing from the gym one morning; I was told he had gone on a Governor's call up.[*]

There was a muzzled air of excitement that pervaded the gymnasium that morning. I sensed, through the special receptors that long term prisoners develop, that somehow it was connected with John's absence. The gym orderlies were walking around smirking, with an 'I know a secret you don't know' look on their faces. Eventually I wheedled it out of one of them. John had gone to the Governor's office to be told the verdict on his parole application. But the punch line was that it was already known in the gym, through the mysterious pipe line of information that exists in prisons, that he had got it. That afternoon he confirmed it. The long vigil of nearly thirteen years was over. His home leave had already been fixed for a month later.

I once tried to thank John for his timely intervention in affairs. He dismissed it casually.

[*] When the Governor wishes to see a prisoner the appropriate wing is notified, and the prisoner has to be present at a specified office at a specified time.

"I'm glad it ended that way," he said. "Sometimes you have to do violence, there is no other way, but in the long run it does no good."

It occurred to me that the policeman who labelled John 'the most dangerous man in Britain', a tag that was eagerly adopted by the tabloid media, one that has acted as a frame for his public image ever since, and one which I suspect he is heartily sick of, should have heard that opinion.

John spent his home leave at the home of one of the professors who had tutored him. When he got back to the Lazy L I was eager to know what it felt like to be out on the outside after so many years.

"Bit strange at first," he said. "I seemed to be out of sync with the pace of daily life. But it all came right when the lad, six year old son of my tutor, grabbed hold of my hand to cross the street. Everything was OK after that, I knew I'd cracked it then. No traumas."

After John had left the Lazy L in those reflective moments when one wonders how life might have been different if such and such had not happened, I wondered how the feud with Lout and Company would have ended if John had not come to the Lazy L. All my conjectures suggested a disastrous end. They might have cut me up. I may have blinded one of them. More remission lost, or an extra prison sentence might have been the result. It didn't bear thinking about. I knew enough about myself to know that to protect the face on my back I would have taken the chance of having my real one cut up; to protect it I was prepared to blind or permanently impair a man's sight. Whichever way it ended, it would have been painful and stupid and pointless. John's authority brought peace; an authority vested in him through the legend; a legend which I am quick to enhance by adding my own story to it whenever I can.

Chapter 26

"Great! Terrific!"

After I had used those words a few times, they came more easily. Usually, I accompanied them with the thumbs up sign to signify satisfaction at what had transpired. It was this pretence which made it worse for me when I was alone; the essence of what I had experienced was not like that at all. Depressed, or dispirited, would have been more appropriate to describe the after-effects of my home leave.

An unbroken residency in different units of Her Majesty's prisons for seven years and one month was interrupted by home leave of one week. In another month I was due to go out permanently. This earlier excursion into the outside world was a preview of the film called life I was supposed to take part in a bit later.

In my day dreams, imagining the future, after I had become acclimatised to the idea that it would be several years before the gates of prison were opened for me, the vision that had remained constant, that was sacrosanct, was seeing myself returning to the big white house on the bend of the country lane, that was my home. I imagined walking up the stone steps, the ridged, sloping cement path, crossing the old flagstones, the green front door, opening it, shutting it, sitting down in the armchair that was traditionally mine. I was at home.

I had waited so long for that simple, yet sustaining fantasy to be fulfilled—and now it was not to be. The intensity of visualizing persistently over a period of time, had created for me a mirage, a ghost, that danced and beckoned from the outskirts, from the perimeter of probability. There was a reason why that ghost was so difficult to exorcise. Even after having known about Daisy's intention to apply for a divorce for about two years, and having had that intention confirmed by my daughter on a recent visit, I still believed there would be some miraculous rearrangement of circumstances, that would prevent it from happening.

One way would have been to present myself on the doorstep and persuade and cajole her to reconsider the whole thing. Whatever had happened between us, however much we had grown apart, we had a common heritage of fourteen years of a reasonably happy, very eventful life together. We had known the life of poverty, and tasted the good life together. Shared memories sometimes act as the only glue that holds together a relationship, when the predilections and passions that first formed it have long since died. Drawing on those shared links with the past to plead my case, I felt I had a very good chance of success.

So, if I could dismount from the high horse of self importance, to meet her in a mood of conciliation, penitence even, for the seven years of hardship my absence had inflicted on her, the situation could be salvaged. There was a third person now, with a vested interest in whether we were divorced or not; with my usual cavalier optimism, I believed I could edge him out of contention.

Because I had not taken an active part in trying to influence matters and, even at this stage the opportunity still existed, is what kept that ghost alive.

The venue for home leave has to be approved by the prison authorities. A friend, recently bereaved, had offered her home in Southampton as a suitable domestic environment at which I could meet my children. Since she was a teacher of long standing, there was no objection. It saved me the humiliation of meeting them in a prisoner's hostel, or similar institution. In agreeing to these arrangements I inadvertently cast myself in a role, for which I was not prepared.

The lady it seemed, had a fixed notion of how a prisoner deprived of sex for a period of seven years should sexually behave: with the speed and urgency of a greyhound out of its trap. I had a more pedestrian expectation, that included such erotic props as bedroom slippers warming by the fire, and cups of hot cocoa. This difference in the levels of our desires created an almost immediate friction.

I was grateful enough for what she had done, but did not know her motive was so primary. My feeling for her had been one of friendship. Through letters and visits over a period of six years, we had maintained contact. When her husband contracted terminal cancer, it coincided approximately with the time I first heard that Daisy wanted a divorce. These circumstances drew us closer together; our letters were more frequent, but there was never more than an anticipation of companionship, and a shared sense of humour in it for me. A friendly kiss and hug on meeting, and parting, at once monthly visits, were the extent of our carnal knowledge of each other.

About my age, in her late forties, she had already been grandmothered several times by prolifically producing offspring. She seemed to enjoy this status, and her handbag usually contained latest photographs of her grandchildren, with appropriate anecdotes for each one. Only seeing her on prison visits for a couple of hours each time, and being given some evidence through stories of her life in Southampton, I drew the wrong picture. I saw a grandmother, against a backdrop of quiet cosiness, in suburbia. I did not imagine there was so much fire to be quenched.

If I had known that firefighting was to be the order of the day, I would have still gone on Home leave—but I would have been psychologically better prepared for it. As it was, it came as an intrusive surprise; my thoughts were concentrated on building a workable relationship with my children. Libidos working at different levels of fervency, and how to synchronize them, was a problem I did not think I would have to cope with on home leave.

I had read enough, been told enough, knew enough by instinct, that after a long period without normal sex a man may have initial difficulties.

However much it is a common day dream among prisoners going out for the first time, to have a sexually receptive partner waiting for them, the fantasy only works out if the partner is of their choosing. In my case it did not help me whatsoever to be met by a woman with a fantasy of her own, supported by a roaring copulatory drive, about a prisoner who would come out of the gates on the run, unzipping his trousers.

The simple uncluttered truth was that she did not evoke in me the physical urge to fulfil her demands; a euphemism for saying that I did not fancy her. I was caught off guard; a little time was needed to adjust to these unforeseen requirements.

I had already failed miserably in the motorway cafe carpark test, failed again, in amongst the trees in the New Forest; the final double-bed test was looming in front of me. It was an examination I was pessimistic about passing.

As the day wore on, my feeling of discomfort and irritability grew; it caused long indifferent silences between us. Already within a few hours of being in her home we were behaving like an ill-matched, close-quartered, married couple of several years standing. Desperately, I drew her attention to the parallel of the man lost in the desert without water. If he does find an odd lake or lagoon in his wanderings, he should not—emphatically, should not—throw himself into it with all his orifices open. Rather, he should approach it sedately, in a dignified fashion, sipping and gargling first, and remembering to wash behind his ears before plunging in. If he were to abandon his reserve at the first sight of water, the shock to his system could be irreparable, and render him permanently incapable of performing any other good works.

How this analogy was received I was unable to say, as by then I was beginning not to look directly at her through a mixture of embarrassment, and annoyance.

My embarrassment was caused by the onset of doubt about my ability to revert to normal sexual procedures, after having used the stimulus of girlie magazines for so long. That doubt had not arisen while I had been in prison, where I had been assured by my peers who had gone through the home leave experience, that it was a bit like riding a bicycle—you never lost your sense of balance. You may not be able to pedal as fast, or be able to execute the tricks and turns of other days; but basically you never forgot how to ride. And certainly I was prepared to ride, at the appropriate time, and do the best I could. But I wasn't prepared for the Alpine section of the Tour de France on my first hour of home leave. I began to wonder if I had become so attuned to the plastic forms portrayed in Playboy, and Penthouse, with artful soft focus lighting, and back-combed pubic hair, that I could no longer cope with the warts and varicose veins of real life sex.

The thought was put to rest almost immediately. I remembered, that even on that first day at the motorway cafe, the pretty girl in the same queue whose eyes had crossed mine briefly, and to whom I had said, "Good morning," and who had smiled back, had started to pump blood to those parts of a man's body that proclaim him well, at least in one department of health, and whose private thoughts at that moment were, "by god, I'm OK, I feel fine, I'm still the same after a seven year lay off."

My annoyance, was because I felt that a person with her accomplishments, (she was doing voluntary work as a Marriage Guidance Councillor) should have known how to handle, what had become a contentious situation, with more finesse. She should have made some allowance for my psychological state of mind, or at least have tried to establish what that state of mind was.

Under the influence of her dissatisfaction at the way our relationship was not taking us to bed, and wanting to win her approval in some other way I offered her my skills as a handyman to do the small jobs her husband might have done if he were alive.

I fixed extra shelves in the kitchen. They fell down. Sweeping up the debris of pickled onions and honey, an adhesive mixture of great potency when spread on an unevenly tiled floor, I muttered into my beard that carpentry had never been my party trick. While this was going on, the lady was glowering at me in a way that suggested that fixing shelves was another thing I couldn't do. Not discouraged, I addressed myself to the problem of the leaking kitchen tap. I fixed it expertly, and sat down to have a well earned cup of tea. I was exhausted; it was the most work I had done for quite some time.

After a few minutes, I noticed a widening semicircle of water seep out from under where I had just fixed the tap. I tried to point out objects of interest to the lady on the other side of the room. She must have wondered what manner of nincompoop she had invited to her home; the other side of the room was a blank wall.

It seems that while I was wrestling with the washer on the tap, I had dislocated another joint further down. This one was of a complexity that even my proficiency as a plumber could not cope with. I gave the injured joint a thick bandage of smelly cloths I found under the sink, and placed a soup bowl under it for the drips. While this was going on, the lady was glowering at me in a way that suggested that fixing taps was another thing I couldn't do.

My most stunning achievement was in the small, very fertile, back garden. There, my experienced eye noticed that the clothesline was sagging, and the clothes in the middle were in danger of trailing on the ground. I told the lady what I proposed to do. She seemed doubtful, almost apprehensive, and warned me that the line was very heavy with all the wet clothes on it. I answered with a snigger of masculine contempt, and exhibited with pantomimic gestures, the strength of my shoulders and biceps. It was difficult to explain to a woman, unversed in man's work, that whereas carpentry and plumbing need a certain amount of abstruse knowledge, raising a clothesline by a couple of feet, only needed brute strength.

I unhooked the line, pulled up the slack, and retied the rope to the nail on the big Bay tree. The clothes were riding high and handsome in the breeze. It was a grand sight, like a small armada of brightly coloured sail boats in the wind. I turned away from the clothesline triumphantly, and indicated my handiwork with a bow and backhand flourish, as is used to unveil a work of art.

At this point there should have been some form of applause from the lady. Why then was she holding her head, groaning loudly, and averting her eyes from something happening behind me? In a state of unconditional disbelief, I heard a sound, quite unmistakable as sounds go, a sort of searing, creaking, frictional sound, that is caused when rope is rapidly slipping off a metal hook. It seems that I had invented a knot whose effectiveness only lasted for a few minutes, after which it unknotted itself and laid its burden down in the mud, and remains of a recent bonfire. While I carried the clothes back to the washing machine, the lady was looking at me in a way that said fixing clotheslines was another thing I couldn't do.

At the washing machine the lady would not allow me to push any of the buttons. She said I had done enough for the day. I myself had come to the same conclusion that I was best suited to just sit and look at the environment, not try to make it better. Sitting on the garden bench in the autumn sunshine, wasps ending their mortal coil around me, I felt lonely, inadequate, useless, disorientated. What was I doing in that strange house? My own was just across the water less than an hour away. I wanted to run there, and beg Daisy to hold me in her arms for ever. All those long, fretful, brooding hours in prison when I had dreamed of going home came back to me. I felt rejected and outcast. Was my absence creating an unseen presence in the long front room that served as dining room and lounge. Were they thinking about me? Talking about me?

They all knew it was my first day of home leave. Earlier that day I had spoken to my sons, and arranged for all of them to come over and spend the weekend with me in Southampton. The thought of how convenient that was, made me realise how indebted I was to my hostess for allowing me that facility.

It lifted the feeling of loneliness that was beginning to envelope me, and brought me back to the problem in hand. The double bed test hung like a storm cloud on the horizon; it carried within it a threat of worsening conditions. I wanted to get it over with, but didn't have the heart to begin.

In the afternoon, around about the time the shelves and the clothesline were falling down, she had looked at me belligerently, and asked if I found her repulsive. She was making vague positional adjustments to her earrings, and recently permed hair, as if she was about to appraise herself in a reflecting surface. In the context, it was an impossible question for me to answer objectively, feeling as I was, that I had been contracted on hire to perform a function, which I was failing to perform; there being a slight misunderstanding between us, as to when I should start working. I could only make a subjective analysis.

No, I did not find her repulsive. Equally no, I did not find her ravishingly alluring. She was somewhere in the middle, where the vast majority of us survive, compromising with our secret desires for famous film stars, politicians, or priests. To each his own delusion. I obviously didn't couch this sentiment persuasively enough, because she became sulky, and distant, for half an hour.

Later, when I started to think about the situation more dispassionately, I saw a reason for my recoiling reaction to her advances. It was so obvious I wondered why I hadn't thought of it right away. Theoretically, intellectually, as far back as I can remember, I have supported the idea of complete equality for as many genders as there may be, in human kind. The lady held the same views. We had no argument on that issue.

So, what's good for the gander etc.; how would the situation look from the other side?

I am the eager, randy, male. She has just been released from prison after seven years. At a motorway stop on the way to my home I initiate a move towards heavy caressing. She puts me off with a laugh, and a joke, that there will be time enough later. In among the trees of the New Forest, I try a grope and a grab—same result. I begin to wonder about her. Is she frigid? Has she, while she was in prison, discovered that she is a lesbian? Circuitously I introduce these questions into the conversation. Just a minute, she says, heatedly, just because I don't drop my knickers instantly on demand, doesn't mean I am a lesbian, or frigid. I can see I have irritated her, and that to continue to pester her to lie down, is going to increase, not lessen, the barrier between us.

Now, at this point, if I persisted in badgering her by related questions around the subject such as, "Do you find me repulsive?" And to sulk if the answer was not an unqualified acclamation of my irresistibility to the opposite sex, surely then, I would be characteristic of the often lampooned male: boorish, crass, insensitive, and selfish.

Her behaviour was precisely according to this hypothesis. And yet, I could not with conviction, label her boorish, crass, insensitive, and selfish. Instead she was making *me* feel unmanly, and less than virile. In trying to arrive at why this was so; why I was reluctant to use those adjectives to describe a woman, I found the clue for the cause of my disinclination to participate in her programme. I was old fashioned. It came as a small self-revealing shock to realise that.

However much lip service I may have paid to the idea of equality between the sexes, when it came to practical demonstrations of an intimate nature, I retreated behind a fortress of social conventions; a stonewalled citadel of custom, and habit, that was a part of my upbringing, and which I had never questioned. One, was a procedural ritual whose ground rules were laid down for me while I was waiting to graduate from short to long trousers. Tradition expected the male of the species to pursue and win the affection of the female. Boys chased after girls, men chased after women; and any ether permutations that were available, and legal, within those heterosexual parameters. Whatever the shortcomings of this arrangement, I had become used to it. Any deviation from this initial routine made me suspicious. I felt uneasy when basic roles were switched.

So that was it. I was mentally disorganized enough with the speed, and choices, of the outside world, I did not want the lady upsetting my precious codes of etiquette as well, on the first day out. It is with these small designs of comportment that the great abstraction called identity is composed. I had clung onto those fragile rafts through the turbulent sea of prison. They were too valuable, if only for reasons of sentiment, to discard so soon.

Once I accepted all that, I felt more confident about taking part in the double bed test. Besides, I had a plan. Puritanical adherence to accustomed ways may be modified if one can approach them from an altered state of consciousness. I decided to get blind drunk that evening.

Accordingly, I agreed to the suggestion that we would have the evening meal at home. Given the choice, I chose rump steak, mushrooms, asparagus, fried onion rings, and green peppers. I did not forget the vital ingredient, a bottle and a half of red wine. I had not tasted some of these things for seven years, and looked forward to the reawakening of those particular tastes on my palate after such a long time.

The lady had temporarily shelved her petulance, and shared my enthusiasm. I helped her to do the shopping at the local supermarket, goggle-eyed with wonder at the opulence of the shelves; there were so many good things to choose from in this land called the Outside. I gave a passing thought to the packet of biscuits and jar of honey I had hidden at the bottom of my bed at the Lazy L, and hoped they were still virgo intacta; I had been forced to leave my cell key with a totally unscrupulous and untrustworthy friend of mine, so that he could water my plants.

I exhibited with that thought that the values of that other land called the Inside had not yet been overturned.

Back in the house, we laid a table with candles, and while the lady, humming a tune conducive to the culinary arts, started to cook, I was given the task of opening the wine. I was feeling much better; this was ground I had trod on a few times before. There was a slight hiccough. The bottle opener was one invented by the creator of the Rubik cube; its purpose was to confound the user by its cleverness. This it did to me, and I chipped the bottle badly. I wasn't going to let the lady see this final disability of mine, so I poured the wine into a jug and hid the bottle in the rubbish bin. My explanation that I had decanted the wine as there was some sediment was accepted.

I had forsworn alcohol for several years after prison hooch had made me ill for a week. I was into my second glass of wine before I realised that I should slow down; it was already having a heady, euphoric effect. All the portents were fine. Cleo Laine and Elke Brooks took it in turn to soothe my ear; the smells from the kitchen won my approval. The land called the Outside was looking rosy.

The meal when it arrived was magnificent. I ate my fill, and drank even more, without discretion or restraint. The lady drank two glasses of wine and got tiddly; I finished the rest of the jug.

After the wine, I found in the lower refrigerated areas of the fridge two cans of beer which I sent down the same way as the wine.

The world was now seen through an insulated haze of alcohol. Conscious awareness seemed to have grown a cushion around it, so that sensations took appreciably longer to get through. I knew I had drunk more than enough, but my course had been set on automatic pilot for outer space.

In a kitchen cupboard, that gave by its contents, the impression that it was only visited at Christmas time, I found a dusty bottle of Cointreau with enough left in it for a couple of hefty nightcaps. It tasted strange, not what I remembered Cointreau to taste like, and I felt on my tongue the texture and shape of what seemed like bits of dried raisins. On examination they proved to be ants.

Trifling details like that were not going to worry me at that stage; I poured the liquid through a tea strainer which reduced the quantity considerably, as there were a lot of ants and they had used the bottle in some kind of a mass burial and embalming rite. After I had drunk that, my memory of the chronology of events, and the events themselves are somewhat vague.

The following day, the lady said I had fallen over a few times. I don't remember that. She also said I had insisted we dance the waltz together, and pointed to a broken ashtray, and wine glass, which were the outcome of that exercise. I don't remember that either. Rather, I had a blurred recollection of watching formation dancing on the television; so perhaps I did at some point get to my feet to demonstrate how it should be done. My memory which was only a series of spasmodic flashbacks anyway, had selected other moments of significance.

I seem to remember that she disappeared for a while. When she came back she was wearing a long, diaphanous, trailing garment. I don't remember laughing raucously, but was told I had. Then somehow, (the intervening stages are a blank) we were in the bedroom. The next flashback is of a sort that fits into the category, that is unworthy of remark when one is in an advanced state of intoxication; the sort of episode that feels quite natural then, but is puzzling as to how it came about, when you think about it the next day.

I was standing, (ah! yes, now I do recall that I fell over at least once) on a small bedside cane stool, declaiming from a book of verses by Omar Khayyam. The mood of the quatrains seemed to express succinctly my state of bacchanalian stupor. So ... the moving finger wrote. The Sultan's tower was caught. And when I looked eastward with outflung arm, I fell over. Unhurt and unabashed, I got back on to my perch and carried on reciting my heart out. I must have got quite carried away with the fervour of it, because it came as a surprise when I heard an exasperated wailing noise. It was the sort of sound one makes when an expression that has been bottled up is finally released. I looked around the room, and located that it was the lady. She was lying on the bed, in a position of hospitality, with the trailing garment draped around her. I heard the noise again, and this time I listened carefully to the words, through dimming consciousness.

"Oh, dear God, no, oh no, not more bloody poetry!" she was howling. "I've had enough of all this philosophical guff. Are we going to fuck, or what? That's what I want to know."

So we did I suppose. That there would be no love in it was understood. What irks me is that I do not know whether there was any lust, or lechery, in it either. I just don't remember anything of the experience.

Chapter 27

The last six weeks at the Lazy L had a misty, dreamlike, distracted quality which hindsight has processed and set in some sort of order. Hindsight has also given me a better understanding of what was happening to me.

Home leave for a long term prisoner is an inspection flight to the mainland of his life, to find out how the world has been getting on without him. For some it turns out to be a bright optimistic vista of what awaits them. I came back groggy, and confused.

On the surface the meeting with my children, grown into adults during my prison sentence, went more smoothly than I had thought it would. I was able with a little effort to recognize a childhood trait, or mannerism, or expression in the faces and forms that had grown so much in those accelerated years of growth. For my part, the physical change in that time was all on the credit side. I had waddled into prison at the age of 38 grossly overweight and dismally unfit. Seven years later I was going out with more grey in my beard, but fit and trim, having shed nearly 30lb of adipose tissue. It was an impressive change.

They came into the lady's house in Southampton button-bright and chirping like birds in the morning. Their familiarity and closeness as a group made it difficult to reach any one of them personally; I merely seemed to preside over the conversation. Most of their talk was of events which were not part of our joint experience. My comments were more and more of the, "Well, I never: Is that so?" variety. It wrapped me in a sense of isolation like a boat stranded on a platform of land, while the others gaily bedecked, certain of purpose and destination, were sailing past me. I felt awkward talking to those teachers and degree holders, nurses and committed political activists, that my children had become.

As a metaphor it was apt; I had been stranded on a seven year Island and didn't know how to join the mainstream of their life again.

It was not as though I was ignorant of world affairs. In prison we are kept abreast of the great happenings on the planet, that war and peace have been declared in diverse parts; that the Russians had moved in somewhere and the Americans were trying to move them out, or the other way around; that Ian Botham had scored a century for England and been arrested for smoking marijuana all on the same day, and that a worn out Borg had thankfully surrendered his Wimbledon crown to McEnroe. On these issues I could join in and be quite articulate.

But the glue that holds together an intimate personal relationship is not knowledge of these events. It is composed of a much simpler adhesive. I would have been better equipped if I had been able to discuss what our odious ex-neighbour really got for his house, or the bad car accident at the end of our lane. But these unhistorical events are not reported in prison. Weekly bulletins from home are needed for that. Our letter writing had been scrappy and superficial. There were great chunks of their lives I knew nothing of.

The question I had dreaded most had not been asked, although I had prepared a half hearted response to it. Then on the day before I was due to go back to prison we went to a leisure centre for the day. I wanted to exhibit my physical condition. The concept of bringing sport to the whole family had been given shape during my seven-year absence, and I had vague notions of getting a job in one of them while I hatched more lucrative plans.

I showed off shamelessly on the badminton and tennis courts; trick shots, funny serves, I gave them the works. My day was made when a man on an adjoining badminton court, whom we had seen play earlier, and who we had observed was pretty good, asked me if I wanted a game. It was a close, hard set but I won: a few people had moved over to one side of the gallery to watch us play; and applauded occasionally. My sons and daughters were grinning and nodding proprietorially at me. It felt fine, as if I was forging a hitherto unseen link with them.

The old, lasting, image of me they must have carried through the prison years was of a tubby presence almost permanently resident in the armchair in front of the TV, and falling asleep at an instant's notice. When I did get up it was only to amble down to the car to go to work at the casino.

Now I was showing them a different me; one with interests and pastimes that made me more reachable than the earlier model; hoping that somehow it would lessen the gap and bring me into their orbit of activities. At least it was a small bridge for further advancement into other areas of their lives.

These hopes became cloudy with misgiving a little later in the leisure centre cafe. Between the tea and the toast one of them asked the question I had been cringing from.

"What are you going to do when you come out?"

Variations of that question had been popped at me at other pivotal times of my life. Thirty five years earlier, along with a few others of similar age, I had been polished and presented to an elder of the tribe, a visiting dignitary, man of wealth and power, whose most-talked of achievement was that he had destroyed more than a hundred tigers in circumstances of unequal combat.

In between recounting his exploits he suddenly turned to me.

"What are you going to do when you grow up, my boy?"

The boy of ten that I was became confused, was not prepared for such a question. I could tell it was important to answer it well; my mother and assorted aunts were smiling, trying not to look strained, hoping I would not say something silly, or worse, not say anything at all. I had a sudden inspiration.

"I am going to shoot tigers," I said hopefully. The great man patted me on the head, and the strain eased away from relatives' faces.

In middle age, my own children around me, I was still not prepared for that question, so answered it in much the same way.

"Well," I said, looking around earnestly, "to start with let me say right away how pleased I am you asked me that. At first, just as a beginning, you know what I mean, I'm going to try and get into one of these,"—I described a circle with my hand that took in the badminton and squash courts, the car park and the swimming pool, in a grand global gesture.

They looked at me dubiously.

"Doing what?" they asked.

I pretended not to hear that, and carried on to expand further.

"Of course, that's only to start with, you know, to get dug in somewhere as they say. What I really want to do is get a job with a team doing research in parapsychology."

They looked at me dubiously again.

"Doing what?" they asked.

I pretended not to hear that one as well, and proceeded to tell them what parapsychology was, making as many anecdotal deviations and including as many boring details as I could think of. After several minutes of concentrated and monotonous drivel, they began to wilt, and nod off. I took that moment to change the subject and order more tea.

The evasiveness had made me feel guilty; shame-faced that I had inaugurated our reunion with a deception. It was as though I had cheated in a matter of honour. It boded no good for our future relationship. And it was while thinking about the possible pattern that relationship might take that I was struck by the realisation that in reality this meeting could well be a reunion to say goodbye. I had no idea where I was going to live nor how I was going to pay for that living. I would be coming out of prison broke, and virtually friendless; such friends as I had left were all in prison.

The lady's offer of a room in her house was the only clear option I had; one in which I could already detect the components of another prison. The thought of having to daily and nightly assuage the fires of her inventive fantasies filled my imagination with discomfiting, mortifying incidents. Just to get myself into sync in the social order was going to be a full-time task; to try and fit in four other personalities into that pattern as well seemed beyond my ability. From the time I had accepted that I was not going back to the family home, I had avoided thinking about it. Home leave had forced me to face the immediate future, and it had alarmed me. I just did not have a clue or inkling as to what I was going to do when I got out. I smothered a desperate impulse to get up from that leisure centre and just keep running; to try and forget everything and everybody connected with my past; to delete from my consciousness all my experiences.

When I came back to prison I did so almost thankfully, telling myself I had five weeks' respite in which to sort matters out in my head.

I was glad to be back in my drab little home with its steel door and iron bars on the window, and the ubiquitous smell of disinfectant seeping in from the corridors. I arrived just before lunch, and during the bang-up period after it, I moved around the cell feeling like a householder returned from a trip, touching familiar objects, giving Ele's trunk a pinch and a punch, checking that my plants had been watered, and that my honey and biscuits had not been touched. While luxuriating in that coming home feeling I understood another aspect of the cumulative effect of long term imprisonment. I felt the first symptoms of an infection I thought I was immune from.

It took me back to an account by Arthur Koestler of a time when he had once been taken out of his cell mistakenly and put on a death train to a concentration camp. The mistake was realised during the journey and he was returned back to his old cell, in the old familiar prison. His relief was so great that he kissed the iron bolts and bars of his cell.

In recalling that story, and recognizing that my underlying feeling was the same, however different in calibration or consequence the two situations were, I had to accept that home leave had given me the perspective to appreciate the truth, the truth that had been hidden from me because it had been seeping into me in such small daily doses. I had caught the disease that is endemic in all long term prisons: I had become institutionalized. How deep that infection was, I would find out when I went out for good, but for the moment I felt downhearted and miserable, more so because I had always thought that I possessed too much in the way of intellectual defences to let that happen to me.

I had a melancholy vision of drifting around aimlessly in a society with a large built-in unemployed population, becoming lost on the trail of impossible dreams, the magnet force of recidivism beckoning always, taking chances, getting caught, and coming back to prison.

I had ascertained while on home leave that as a single un-employed person I could expect twenty two pounds a week from the state. The lady had offered me room and board in her house for £10 a week, on condition I helped her with some odd jobs around her bedroom. That left me £12 to spend wildly on bus rides and newspapers. Soon my reckless personality would crave the high life of having coffees in cafes, and going to the cinema. To pay for that lifestyle I would turn to...and then there I would be, back in the boob.

Except for some miraculous opportunity that might come my way I could not envisage any other outcome. I had no qualifications.

All the innovative ability, and will to overcome obstacles that had once made me a successful entrepreneur, seemed to have evaporated during the years in prison. The institutional regime had suffocated it; the battery-farm existence where the basics of life, food, drink, clothing, shelter, were provided free of cost. Doctors, dentists, specialists, priests, psychologists, professional visitors, were all available a short walk away from one's dwelling. And if the quality of these practicioners was not of the highest calibre, it was only rarely that a prisoner died of their ministrations. Even the luxuries of entertainment, sport, education, hobbies, were provided within the precincts of the prison.

Cocooned and spoonfed for several years, all but the most recal-citrant are seduced to the inevitable easy life, and eventually all in-itiative and gumption are lost. The prisoner expects his guardian to arrange everything for him. Institutionalism leaks into him at every level until he is completely saturated. His attitude becomes more and more like that of a farmyard animal looking always to the good shepherd for sustenance.

I tried to cover up my depression by telling my peers how well home leave had gone, and listed the number of golden opportunities that awaited me on my release. It was no use, in fact it made it much worse for me when I was alone. I became two people; one that laughed and joked easily, a person of good spirits, an optimist who was going out to an eventful and comfortable life outside; and the other who lay painfully wide awake at nights, chewing his fingernails, a pessimist who believed that he was destined to live in prison all his life.

I started having bad dreams, in much the same way as I had when I first came into prison. Mostly it was the same one in which I was cornered by something I could not make out, but which I knew was terrifying. I used to wake up with a bang, heart racing, as though I had just come off the badminton court. The feeling on awakening was as if I had been on the verge of uttering the answer to an important question; one which would forever elude me.

After about a week of that I decided to see one of the prison psychologists. It was ironical that what the anguish of imprisonment had not done was achieved by the trauma of liberation. For the first time in my prison career I was voluntarily visiting a psychologist.

He turned out to be a short, fat, pale, man in a dark crumpled suit, who used his lower lip from time to time as a ledge on which to rest the stem of a moist pipe. He looked tired and fed up with his lot in life. I judged him to be in his early fifties.

He pulled his features into an expression that was meant to suggest interest.

"What can I do you for?" he asked. I decided to present my case obliquely to keep his interest.

"I have an unusual request to make," I began, "I have come to ask you whether you would support me in an application to the Governor so that I may be permitted to stay on for an extra three months in prison."

I looked to see how he was taking it. He was looking bored, rubbing his eyes with pudgy fingers.

"I said," leaning forward speaking more emphatically, "I want to stop on a bit longer in prison. Do you hear me?"

"Loud and clear," he said, "I heard you the first time. As it happens it is not an unusual request, but of course as you must already know, out of the question."

"It is not an unusual request?" I countered, slightly flabbergasted.

"No, not really," he replied. "Normally it is not so bluntly put, but by and large I've heard that request before, yes."

He glanced at some papers on his desk. Clenched his pipe between his teeth and looked at me earnestly.

"You've just been on home leave, right? After seven years inside, right? And what you are now saying is that you need more time to adjust and that it is all very fast and difficult, right?"

"Right," I said.

"Quite natural, so would I be if I was in your position."

He asked me to tell him about home leave. What I had done, whom I had seen and so on. After I had finished he looked at me quite angrily.

"So what are you moaning about?" he asked. "Here you are describing a high level life, rushing off to leisure centres, Indian restaurants and all that. Let me tell you, my friend, that I am nearly forty and never been inside one of those leisure places." He made it sound as if Leisure centres were the pits of degeneration.

I commiserated with him for having reached the age of forty so quickly. He looked at least fifty-five; the sort of man who seems to solidify into advanced age as a matter of fashion while still quite young.

I felt a growing irritation at myself for having sought help from this narrow-minded little man who thought there could be nothing wrong with a person who went to leisure centres. I got up to leave. As I was going through the door, he waved his pipe at me emphatically.

"I'm going to give you a piece of advice, which I hope you will refer to," he said.

He jabbed the air in front of him with his pipe a few more times for emphasis.

"Today is the tomorrow you worried about yesterday. Think about that. You'd be surprised how many of you blokes I've helped with that."

He was smiling at me fatuously as though he was expecting applause. There was such an air of righteous satisfaction in his tone, it made me turn back into the room. He looked momentarily alarmed. His right hand dropped out of sight where the emergency buzzer was located; it was after all a high-security prison which contained a lot of violent people.

"I've just had a great idea," I said, smiling enthusiastically.

"Why don't you get that printed in large letters and have it mounted under a photograph of yourself, something austere and wise-looking if your features can cope with that formation, and leave it on that chair. You could then stay at home and grow old gracefully in Leisure centres."

He was making interruptive shapes with his mouth, opening and closing it like a fish in trouble, but I didn't let him speak.

"You could even," I continued, "have some piped music to go with it which began as the door opened; something with a hook to it like a TV advertisement. Then the popularity of your quite useless little bromide could be judged by the number of convicts whistling it in the exercise yard."

He was looking quite bemused as I left him. Although he had done nothing to dispel any of my apprehensions I felt better for having expressed my frustration in the way I had. It buttressed my opinion that the practice of psychology in prisons is another one of those useless exercises aimed not so much for the relief of those it purports to help, but to give the institution itself more stability, a broader base; to give it more credibility as a necessary adjunct of modern life; and thereby to create these unreal mastodons that seem indispensable to society, because people of so many varied disciplines are employed to service it.

Having got nothing of value from the psychologist I looked for a therapy figuratively and literally closer to home.

During the last few months at the Lazy L I had become friendly with a man called Phil. He was finishing a fifteen year sentence for a series of violent offences, committed during his membership of an inner city firm whose most lucrative lines were extortion, and prostitution. His own department was hurting people, mostly women, to make them see the point of view of the firm's executives. He was by his own account, and by his track record, a brutal and merciless man.

One night, three years into his sentence, he saw an orange glow like a fire at the foot of his bed in a cell in Wormwood Scrubs. In the middle of the orange glow there was this face of Christ. Phil told me he recognized him right away by the head band, and the cut of his beard. During the ensuing conversation a conversion was effected. The cruel man of violence was tenderised into an angel of love and goodwill, who daily tried to exhibit his new faith—sometimes to the acute consternation of his unconverted colleagues.

On one occasion he came out on exercise with a bar of white Windsor soap, a towel, and a bowl of water asking anyone who passed by if he might wash their feet.

He asked me. I declined the offer.

"Don't be so proud, Kris," he had said. "If our Lord did it, I'm prepared to do it too." Then switching to a prophetic, biblical voice he added, "And who shall gainsay me."

It was generally felt that he would get nutted off[*] if he kept that

* certified insane.

up. But even the hard men of rationality, doctors and medical staff, were loathe to commit a man to a lunatic asylum whose only fault seemed to be that he wanted to emulate the life of Jesus.

During the early years of his reformation it was thought that he was grafting for parole, using religion as a means to further his chances. If that were true, it hadn't worked. He actually served ten years of his sentence, and was due to leave the prison at about the same time as me.

I told him of my fears.

He said, "Suffer little children to come unto me for theirs is the kingdom of heaven."

He then outlined a brilliant plan. He said we should put together all the dope we could muster between us, and go on an intensive dope smoking binge for the last four weeks of our time in prison. In between the dope smoking he said he would pray and meditate on my behalf. Jesus himself, he said, was not averse to a nibble at a hallucinatory mushroom from time to time, and since they weren't readily available in prison we should use what we could get.

"And who shall gainsay us?" I said.

He liked that.

"And we shall dwell in the house of the Lord for ever and ever," he added.

After we had scraped together all our debts for arrangements we had made for other prisoners while we were on home leave, our joint stock was about four ounces. Considering the way we smoked it, a match head at a time on a pipe, it would have, under normal circumstances, lasted us about three months.

Phil's belief was that if we got stoned every waking moment of our time Jesus would visit us with words of advice on how I should conduct myself when I went out. Phil also said that Jesus quite often spoke through him, so I should watch out for his words.

I agreed to do anything he suggested, just so long as it involved smoking all the dope. I did not think Jesus would be interested in my post-release problems but there was a blazing intensity in Phil's eyes when he spoke of religious matters that dissuaded listeners from contradicting him, in case he suddenly lost control.

We started that same night and carried on for a week nonstop. I abandoned all sporting activities, in fact I abandoned all other interests in favour of dope smoking. Phil ceaselessly pounded my ears about Christ and his adventures.

Then, during the early part of the second week I awoke one morning with a delicious sense of anticipation. It was the sort of feeling children have on the morning of a birthday when some incredible present has been promised them. The world was different. It had become flawless. Beauty was everywhere. Everything I looked at was beautiful; the design on my quilt, the sunlight through the cobwebs, the flakes of rust on the bars. Everything. And the smells! The new-mown grass outside my window, the breakfast trolley outside my door. And the sounds! The addictive musicality of reciting the conjugation of a Spanish verb. Everything I heard was melodious.

I wandered around as in a dream, not knowing what was happening; but that it was wonderful. Some safety valve faculty in my brain warned me that this extraordinary consciousness was not good; that it was like the effects of a powerful drug which was fine while it lasted but left the seeds of devastation in its wake. And yet the sensation was one of calmness, of spiritual satisfaction, which I could not associate with anything bad. It was as though I had had some deep revelation in my sleep which had opened up all my senses in the most benevolent way. I had a strong cognition that a bad chapter of my life had ended and a wonderful new one was about to begin.

I hurried over to Phil's for the usual prebreakfast pipes, but I did not know how to tell him of the sensations I was experiencing. It would have sounded too theatrical, as though I had invented it to please him. He had never stopped telling me that Jesus was due to visit me any night in an orange glow at the end of my bed.

As soon as I sat down he poured out a mug of tea and asked me as he always did in the morning if I had seen any visions, ghosts, apparitions, or anything significant during the night.

In saying no to him I felt guilty, not to say uncertain, in allowing the possibility that his supplications to Jesus had anything to do with the way I was feeling.

Something had happened to me during the night, a dream, illusion or hallucination had occurred which had left me this legacy of mystical euphoria. But to attribute it to one particular religious figure seemed somehow inappropriate.

I also discounted the possibility that it was the cumulative effect of the dope I had been smoking, because such sensations as dope produces, although similar, were both short-lived and qualitatively different. This sort of prolonged joy was something outside my range of experiences.

So I went through the day in wondering ecstasy, wanting to clap my hands and laugh out aloud over nothing, and having to restrain myself from doing so. Every now and again I would get a warning flash that it was not natural to feel that good, but those signals were very transitory, and I was back to being stunned by the minutiae of my daily life; the incredible visual satisfaction in looking at the kaleidoscope of colours around a pigeon's neck, or being transfixed by the fascinating pictures I could see on a partially damp wall.

Once or twice during this period I thought about my unease at having to tackle the hurdles of the outside world. The problem seemed distant, academic, as though it was not pertinent to me; a conundrum of life, somebody else's life, that teased my intellect in a pleasant sort of way as a jigsaw puzzle might, with no degree of urgency. I was incapable of getting depressed about it any longer, even though I had no solutions. Every second, minute, hour, of my day was so full of interest that I could not conceive of a date two weeks away.

The only way in which I could respond was to chuckle cosily to myself that it would all work out right on the day. If I had been told then that I was to be executed in two weeks' time, I believe I would have accepted it quite amicably, and thought it would all work out right on the day. Nothing seemed important enough to get worried about. I was so enslaved by the impact the world around me was having on my senses that there seemed to be no time for anything else.

An instance of this intense fixation with the routine events of my day came in the kitchen. I was waiting for milk to boil in a metal container without a handle; one had to be very adept at milk-watching not to let it froth over. As the milk started to heat up I became riveted by the formation of the first bubbles of air and then in the heaving and turning of the liquid.

It suggested to my imagination the evolution of a planet. The volcanic upheavals were miniaturised for me. I was looking at the world being made. And when the milk boiled over and flowed down the sides like lava down a mountainside I was still watching attentively and saying, "Wow! Look at that, it must have been like that in the beginning."

I heard the voice of the kitchen cleaner harsh with self interest, shouting, "Fuck the beginning. Whatsa matter with you? You crackin' up or what? I got to clean that up in the morning." It brought me back to a sense of reality.

I somehow formed the conviction during that day that if I told anybody about what I was experiencing it would immediately disappear. Later on when I was able to think rationally about those amazing hours I would come to think of it as the William Blake period of my life when I saw the World in a bowl of milk.

After two days I began to see the contours of the real world through the dream. All the cracks and imperfections and doubts were still there. The world was no longer perfect. Colours and patterns were no longer so compelling; sounds were no longer so dulcet; the critical faculty was restored to taste; not everything I ate was a feast anymore.

The aftermath, the coming down from the high plane of consciousness, that I reckoned would be painful, was not so. Normality seeped back into me quite naturally without any jarring side effects. I felt calm and assured. It was as though I had been given a spiritual bath which had left me clean. I no longer felt depressed or unprepared to be going out to face the world.

All the tension had been washed out of me by the experience. How or why it happened remains a mystery to me. If it was an illumination in the Christian sense, it left me with no greater sensitivity for Christianity or Christ. If it was the cannabis, then it was unique, as I have since then smoked as much and more, without the same effect. Or yet, was it that twilight area of consciousness that is supposed to precede a nervous breakdown? I don't know. And perhaps, not to lessen the mystical significance, it is best that I never know. Giving something like that a name kills the magic of it.

About a week before my release I was going through my shelf of books. The prison rule was that a prisoner could take out with him only those books which appeared on his property sheet, which indicated that they had been sent in to him. Books which had been borrowed or bought from other prisoners had to be left behind.

Sorting through them after a seven year two month accumulation was a nostalgic experience, as usually they contained an inscription which brought back a memory of the donor. One of the books was six years old and had a birthday message on the flyleaf. It was from my children. I worked out by the date that they must have been sixteen down to eleven years old when they had sent that.

It set me thinking of them again, trying to conceive of a way of life which would enable me to see them—regularly. As a result of going to prison I had lost my wife and home. That was bad enough. I was determined not to let the prison sentence rob me of my whole family.

I sat down with the book in my hands. It was a world atlas and as I leafed idly through the pages thinking, quite abruptly, I knew what I had to do. The revelation came to me in much the same way as finding an object in front of your face that you have been looking all over the house for.

It was so blatantly simple, yet so exciting. I made myself an extra strong joint to celebrate; it was not really necessary as I had been keeping up wholeheartedly with Phil's plan and was quite stoned anyway.

It was perhaps because I was stoned that I began to imagine I was a top executive planning a commercial campaign and started to jot it all down. I made headings and subgroups, and hoped it would be as impressive the next morning as it appeared that night. Too often the brilliant idea of the night before looks utterly infantile the next morning. But occasionally an idea that is born of a stoned mind retains some of its originality.

I wrote down AIMS on the top of the page. Under it I wrote down all that I wanted to achieve in the relationship with my children. I hadn't got very far with that to realise that what I really wanted was friendship with them. Being their father was not important at all. Friendship allows no room for pretensions; it is by convention a more honourable relationship, binding people who like one another, rather than fatherhood ever could be with its expected sentiments, and suffocating protocol.

Fatherhood out, friendship in—I wrote as a sub heading.

How to achieve that friendship headed another list. First I would take up residence in the lady's house. Then I would invite them over one at a time; group meetings were out. They tended to give joint answers to individual questions. I must talk to them, go out with them, get to know them... and it was at that point in my ruminations that the revelation had struck me. So simple it was. I must be truthful and honest with them the way friends are to one another. I underlined the two words and stared at them.

I would never again tell them lies about doing research in parapsychology, or looking for a job sweeping floors, and stacking up chairs in a leisure centre. I would tell them I hadn't a clue what I was going to do.

They would either be my friends and love me as I stood with all my imperfections, or I would be nothing to them. I would be their friend and love them as they stood with all their faults, or I would rather they were strangers to me.

By the time I went to bed that night I was brimming with confidence. I knew I would succeed. If there was one attribute I possessed it was the ability to make and maintain friendships.

After that, the turmoil that is called 'gate fever' by long-term prisoners subsided within me. I slept soundly the night before the day of my release. And on the day, my hand did not shake as I signed my release papers, and pocketed the forty one pound handout.

The clothes I had worn into prison, smart and fashionable at the time, hung on me like a pyjama suit. I left them in the cardboard box they had lain in for so many years, and put on the prison issue denim suit.

Outside in the late August sunshine I paused at the intersection at the end of the country lane on which the prison stood.

I did not know whether to turn left or right. What I did know was that I was not going straight.

KRIS.

WHERE ARE YOU NOW —
IN YOUR LIFE?

I am in the sequel of
my life inside. Then what
happened?

Kris.